ST ALBION
PARISH NEWS

BOOK 9

Published in Great Britain by
Private Eye Productions Ltd, 6 Carlisle Street, W1D 3BN.
© 2006 Pressdram Ltd
ISBN 1 901784 44 4
Designed by Bridget Tisdall
Printed and bound by
Butler and Tanner Ltd, Frome and London
2 4 6 8 10 9 7 5 3 1

NEW VICAR PLEASE!

THE LAST DAYS OF
THE REVEREND TONY BLAIR

ST ALBION PARISH NEWS BOOK 9
Further letters from the vicar,
the Rev. A.R.P. Blair MA (Oxon)

compiled for

PRIVATE EYE

by Ian Hislop, Richard Ingrams,
Christopher Booker and Barry Fantoni

PARISH PORTRAITS NO. 94

The Vicar writes:

Mr Brown is seen here saying his prayers and asking God to forgive him for what he has been up to in the last year. I don't know about the Almighty, but I'm not sure that I will! T.B.

ST ALBION PARISH NEWS

16th September 2005

Hullo!

And there's only really been one thing happening in the past
couple of weeks – no, not the hurricane, Dean, although of course
that's very sad and we're all very sorry for our good friend the Rev.
Dubya, who frankly cannot be blamed for what's happened, which
was an Act of God, and, honestly, to blame the Rev. Dubya for it is
like blaming Noah for the flood, when all he was trying to do was
to save everyone!

Anyway, it's only too easy, isn't it, to blame the man in charge
when something goes wrong – when usually it is not their fault at
all, but that of lots of other people below them who aren't up to the
job, such as Mr Byers... but I digress.

It's not the hurricane that's the important thing. I know from all
your letters and emails and texts that what really concerns you on
a day-to-day basis is the flood of loutish and anti-social behaviour
that is engulfing the streets of our parish!

Everywhere we look we see young people behaving badly
– stuffing their lager cans into people's garden hedges, spitting out
their chewing gum onto our pavements, spraying graffiti on the
walls of the bus shelter, and – I'm sorry to say it – drunkenness,
drunkenness, drunkenness. The 'Three D's', as I call them!

Well, it really doesn't have to be like that!

And I've thought long and hard about how to tackle this
problem. No, Vijay, I'm not going to resign. That's not funny or
clever. In fact, it's an example of precisely the kind of rude, nasty,
thoughtless behaviour that I am determined to stamp out, right
across the parish.

And that's why I've come up with my Two-Point Plan, which
I've called my 'Respect Plan'.

1. To alleviate the problem of drunkenness, the Britannia Arms
should remain open for 24 hours a day, so that everyone will be
free to continue drinking steadily and in a civilised manner, rather
than having to indulge in binge-drinking sessions just because the
pub is about to close. Makes sense, doesn't it?

2. I have asked my good friend Mrs Casey to become the St
Albion's Respect 'czar', spearheading our new campaign to teach
the kids how to behave properly.

And, hey, let's admit it. It's not just the kids who get drunk and swear and create a thorough nuisance of themselves.

It's Mrs Casey as well! And that's the whole point of why I have appointed her! You all remember the scene she created at the Harvest Supper, when she knocked back a whole bottle of Communion wine and started swearing at everyone.

Some of the older parishioners may have been shocked when she described the PCC as "a bunch of w***ers" and suggested that it was a good idea to be drunk all the time because it helps you to work better.

But I take a different view. The very fact that Mrs Casey is a foul-mouthed alcoholic makes her ideally qualified to head up our Anti-Social Behaviour Task Force, because she knows just where these kids are coming from! Ok?

Which brings me to my second point. As I'm sure you know, I have recently returned from our mission to China, where I have been preaching the word to our Chinese brethren.

It was a very successful and enlightening trip, with both sides learning a great deal about each other's spiritual point of view!

Cherie came along with me, and was delighted to be able to get some early Christmas shopping, when she bought several hundred bras and T-shirts for only the equivalent of 20p! It's hard to think that children of five can make such wonderful garments! There's a lesson there for our own five-year-olds who are getting drunk and falling around in the streets!

Anyway, much to my surprise, our hosts invited me to play a game of football.

Some reports in our local media have tried to suggest that I kept missing the goal. But let me say, it is they, the journalists, who have 'missed' the point! Of course I wasn't trying to kick the ball into the goal.

I was deliberately missing the goal, and for a very good reason. 'Respect' for my Chinese hosts, who are very sensitive about losing face. In fact you can even be locked up if you cause offence or upset them!

As seen by local artist Mr de la Nougerede.

So can we please hear no more about our vicar 'missing the target', because that's one thing I never do!

Which brings me back to my first point, which is the

theme of this newsletter. The three 'R's' – 'Respect', 'Respect' and 'Respect'.

Which is why, for this week's evening service, I have written a new chorus to remind us all of how important it is to show respect to each other.

Respect, respect, respect,
It's what we all expect,
Respect, respect, respect,
It's what we mustn't neglect!

Words and music T. Blair 2005

(Taken from '100 Hymns For Binge-Drinkers', which can be downloaded onto your iPod from the vicarage website www.welovetony.org)

Yours 'respectfully',

Tony

A Message From Rev. Dubya Of The Church Of The Latter-Day Morons

Brothers and sisters in New Englandland Land – I thank you all for your prayerfulness and your condolleezences at this time of despairitude.

But make no mistake – this is the work of the Lord, as is foretold in the Words of the Prophet, "Yea, there shall come a mighty wind and great waves and ye shall do damn all about it".

Thus saith the Lord and who am I to question the will of the Almighty?

No, siree! My job is to watch and pray. Pray and watch. Look at my watch and pray that everything turns out ok as time ticks away for poor old Dubya!

So my congratuity goes out to you all again in my hour of needfulnosity.

And my message to all you drowning black folks in Noo Orleans – Hang on in there, a piece of my old ma's cherry pie is coming your way, courtesy of Brother Rumsfeld's Heat-'n'-Eat CherryPieToGo Corporation, which is looking after all your wants in this hour of your death!

God be with you, for I am not.

Rev. Dubya

ST ALBION PARISH NEWS

30th September 2005

Hullo!

And in this week of the annual parish outing, when we all go off together to the seaside at Brighton to take stock and to plan the year ahead, it is obviously my job to tell you all where we are going.

It's what we call a 'mission statement', from the Latin words 'missio', meaning 'a mess' and 'statementum', meaning 'the state that we're in'!

So let's begin with what we're NOT going to do. Let's get the negatives out of the way first, shall we! The first thing we are NOT going to do is to go back to the bad old days of the past, as some of the older people in the parish would like us to do!

And not just the old people, either! There are some people closer to home (well, close to my home, anyway!) who still seem to be hankering after those comfortable old certainties of yesteryear that the rest of us left behind a long time ago!

And no one knows better than me how tempting it is to get a round of applause at the outing by singing the old hymns and preaching the old sermons!

But, hey, I'm Tony, remember? A modern vicar telling it like it is, not like it was! We're living in 2005, you know, not 1926, or wherever else certain people think we should be going back to.

It's all very well to drone on in a sanctimonious Scottish accent about the old values, the old dogmas and the old creeds (y-a-a-a-wn!!!).

But that's hardly going to sort out the problems of a modern church trying to go forward in the fast-changing world of today! Look, in this life we all have to accept that there's a congestion charge, and we all of us just have to pay up and drive on (thanks for that clever image to our friend, Mr Livingstone!).

And talking of Mr Livingstone, it would be nice to see you here in church, Ken, from time to time, rather than in the new mosque, where I gather you've lately become rather a celebrity!

Anyway, that brings me to my second point in my 'To Do' list of things that we are NOT going to do. Whatever a lot of people in the parish may have been saying, I can tell you that we are NOT, repeat NOT, going to 'cut and run'!

I am referring, of course, to all those fainthearts who are calling for us to desert our good friend the Rev. Dubya of the Church of the Latter-Day Morons, and to abandon his great crusade to make the world a more dangerous place. *(Is this right? Ed.)*

I was even accosted by our friend in the wonderful new enlarged Tesco (where the golf course used to be) – standing next to the new 'Cheese 'n' Home Loans Counter, Buy One, Get One Free' – saying, in his usual unhelpful way, "Why don't you admit it, Reverend? You got it all wrong, didn't you?".

"Why don't you just cut and run, Vicar?", he shouted, as I accidentally pushed him into the bags of charcoal lining the 'BBQ and Personal Finance' aisle.

And there's that phrase again – 'Cut and run'. It's oh-so-tempting, isn't it, when faced with life's difficulties, to look for the quick exit, the easy way out!

But, you know, the easy option is very often the wrong one. It may be an old-fashioned word, 'wrong'. But I'm afraid it's the only one which will do in this context.

Anyone remember those old-fashioned phrases, such as 'In for the long haul', 'Sticking at it' and 'Seeing the job through'? Because that, my friends, is exactly what your vicar's planning to do.

So that when, in years to come, future generations of Albionians look back on our time, they will say, "Remember the Rev. Blair? He didn't cut and run! He didn't listen to what everyone said. He saw the job through!".

In fact, I've composed a chorus that you can all sing on the coach on our way home from the seaside:

Don't cut and run,
See the job through.
Stick to your guns,
It's got to be true.
(Repeat)
Words and music T. Blair.

Or, as our good friend Mr Mandelson so neatly put it on his business cards, "I'm a fighter, not a quitter".

Doesn't Peter speak for all of us, with those brave words? I know he speaks for me!

Yours (to the end),

Tony

✝ To Remember In Your Prayers

● Mr Lance Price, who many of you will not have heard of, but who used to work at the vicarage helping out Mr Campbell with preparing this newsletter.

Unfortunately, Mr Price seems to have had some sort of nervous breakdown and, no doubt as part of his therapy, has seen fit to write a 'book' about his years working in a lowly capacity behind the scenes here at the vicarage.

I think the title of his book, *'My Years At The Vicarage Photocopier'*, tells us everything we need to know! Telling lies is never very nice and can get you into a lot of trouble – not that I would know! Anyway, let us pray that Mr Price is able to enjoy to the full the '30 pieces of silver' he has received for his 'memoirs', as he attempts to start a new life in France with his male 'partner'. T.B.

Congratulations!!!

We were all delighted to hear our good friend Mr Kennedy, minister of the United Reformed Liberal Democratic Church, frankly admitting to his congregation that he had made an awful mess of leading his flock and was really not up to the job!

Of course, many of us have known this for ages, particularly with his fondness for the bottle and his pathetic attempts to win popularity by becoming a father rather too late in life!

But it is always good to hear someone owning up to their failings, and on that score, we must give Mr Kennedy his due for being ready to admit what a hopeless failure he has been! Well done, Charles!

The only sensible course for him now is to cut and run! T.B.

KIDZ KORNER

● Have you heard this latest joke doing the rounds of the St Albion Primary School Playground (shortly to be our new Tesco car park)?

Q: *Is the Vicar in denial over Iraq?*

A: *No, he's in de Tigris and de Euphrates!*

(Thanks to Mr Bremner for this one! T.B.)

Poor Mr Kennedy makes a Charlie of himself! As seen by local artist Mr de la Nougerede

ST ALBION PARISH NEWS

14th October 2005

Hullo!

And what an outstanding success – yet again – was this year's annual parish outing to sunny Brighton!

What a pity therefore that some people have got it into their heads that the only thing which happened was the unfortunate incident involving one of our OAPs, Mr Wolfgang Amadeus Looney *(I think I've got that right? Please check).*

Let me say right away that I have already offered Mr Looney my unreserved apologies, as have many other members of the PCC, including Mr Straw, whose important address in support of our good friend the Rev. Dubya, Mr Looney so unforgivably interrupted!

Hey, no one likes to see an old man being chucked out onto the seafront by 'bouncers'. But the fact is that I wasn't even there when Mr Looney was kicked out so, frankly, it was nothing to do with me, which makes it all the more commendable that I should have offered him my apologies!

It's hard enough for any of us to say sorry, isn't it? But how much more difficult it is to say sorry for something you haven't done!

"That's when a big man walks tall", to quote my friend the Rev. Dubya, as Mr Straw was doing when he was so rudely heckled by this senile old man, shouting obscenities and casting a shadow over what was otherwise a glorious day out for us all!

So let's draw a line, shall we, under the whole subject of Mr Looney, who is I gather having treatment in the geriatric wing of the St Albion's Hospital for the Mentally Handicapped (shortly to be redeveloped as our new Tesco's)?

But before we move on, let's just spend a few minutes looking at where Mr Looney is coming from. In his day – which was, I'm afraid, quite a long time ago – it was considered perfectly acceptable to disagree with people, and even to interrupt them when they were talking!

Not very modern, that kind of behaviour, is it? Nowadays we have moved on from that kind of negative 'debate'!

Now we all agree on what we think, so there is no need for anyone to step gratuitously out of line just because they want to make a point (and also, frankly, because they may be suffering from a nervous breakdown!).

**The Vicar's Dream! As seen by local artist
Mr de la Nougerede**

In today's church, thank goodness, we are all singing from the same hymn sheet. And if we don't, we shouldn't be surprised if we find that we are thrown out into the street by highly-trained anti-terrorist churchwardens, as quite rightly happened to Mr Looney!

And speaking of terrorism, didn't Mr Looney wear a badge proclaiming his loyalty to a notorious and dangerous organisation associated with bombs – the so-called 'CND'?

How were our gallant churchwardens meant to know that Mr Looney was not a suicide bomber, concealing a ton of high-explosive beneath his dirty old anorak?

Hey, I've apologised for what happened, but don't you think it is Mr Looney who should be apologising to me?

And to the rest of you as well, who might not be alive today if it hadn't been for the prompt 'firm but fair' action of our security staff who risk their lives daily keeping at bay the likes of Mr Looney, with their crazed ideas of a world dominated by Muslim terrorists.

So let me say that I am happy to accept Mr Looney's apology for his disgraceful behaviour at Brighton, which completely ruined our entire outing, by distracting attention from my own inspiring speech!

Just to remind you, I spoke about all my plans for the parish over the next ten years, and above all my determination to stay on as vicar for as long as it takes, and until a worthy successor finally emerges!

I leave you with this thought. Perhaps Mr Milburn, our former curate, may be ready for the job in a few years' time.

Go for it, Alan!

Yours ever, Tony

PS. I am sorry that we have not had enough space in this newsletter to reprint our treasurer Mr Brown's annual address to the parish. But any parishioners who are interested (probably not a huge number!) can go on the website and read last year's speech, which was much the same (except that this year he's got his figures even more wrong than before!).

A Message From God as told to Rev. Dubya Bush Of The Church Of The Latter-Day Morons

Well done thou good and faithful servant Dubya! When I didst bid thee to go forth to Iraqistan and verily smite ass thou didst so – yea, verily, yea!

And now when I biddest thee to go smite butt in Iranland I know ye will not fail me even unto the end of the world – which it mighteth well come to – but who careth?! It's all in the cause of defeating the Evil One!!

So stand tall Dubya, mounteth thy trusty steed and DOETH WHAT A MAN HATH GOTTETH TO DOETH.
    GOD.

PS: Thus spake myself the Lord to Rev. Dubya and I commandeth him to pass it on to his brother in old Englandland, Pastor Toby Bloom and his lovely wife Cherry Pie.

St Albion's Primary School
Mrs Kelly writes:

We are now well into the Ramadan term (what we used to call autumn) and I would like to remind parents that the most important contribution the school can make to their children's education is my drive to stamp out fizzy drinks, crisps, sweets and above all those dreadful 'Turkey Twizzlers' that we saw on Jamie Oliver's wonderful TV series! Already we have achieved spectacular results in achieving our 'Eat Well Targets'. 83 percent of children have not eaten Turkey Twizzlers this term at all – due to the fact that they have a 100 percent truancy record and have not attended school yet this term.

So congratulations all round!

— Salve —

A big welcome to our latest overseas visitor, Father Putin of the Russian Extremely Orthodox Church. Patriarch Putin can certainly teach us a thing or two about how to keep order, and he congratulated me on my handling of the dissident Mr Looney. "You should have packed him off to the Siberian salt mines," joked the jovial Soviet Man-of-God, "like I do with all the businessmen whose property I wish to confiscate!" I joked back that we in St Albion's could hardly send people to the salt mines, since Mrs Hewitt is having a crackdown on salt, as it is bad for people's health! "That's the whole idea", quipped my irrepressible Russian friend!
                                                  T. B.

ST ALBION PARISH NEWS

28th October 2005

Hullo,

Which, by the way, is my catch-phrase, although you've probably been hearing rather a lot of it lately from a certain young parishioner who's taken it into his head that he's me!

I think his name is David Something-or-other, and you've probably seen him hanging around outside the new Tesco's (formerly the St Albion's Cottage Hospital), handing out leaflets and telling people about his "Third Way"!

And you're not going to believe this, he's even claiming that he's the rightful vicar!

And what's really sad about this chap, something Cameron I think he calls himself, is that he stands there like an idiot, smiling a lot and trying to ingratiate himself with everyone by using matey phrases, such as "look", "hey" and even "hullo".

Hey look, I don't want to be judgemental, but this poor young man clearly needs help!

And the way he parades his wife and toddler around the parish is, frankly, sickening!

Goodness me, what would people in the parish think if I started sending out Christmas cards with pictures of my wife and children on them?

I can tell you, Cherie and little Leo would never forgive me!

Can I just tell you a short story at this point? I was giving little Leo a bath the other night, allowing Cherie a well-earned night off in Kuala Lumpar where she'd been invited to sign copies of the Malaysian edition of her wonderful book about life in the vicarage.

And you know what he said to me? "Daddy, I'm so pleased that you've made time to give me the benefit of your parenting skills, one of which of course is guarding my privacy."

Bless! "Out of the mouths of babes," as it says in the New Labour Bible, "you shall hear some really great stuff about the vicar" (*Book of Sudoku*).

But back to our poor deluded friend, Mr Cameron. I don't want to go on about him, but at the end of the day, you know, he just talks in platitudes!

I've tried to listen to him, but, frankly, it's all a lot of empty nonsense! Verbal candyfloss!

I mean, he stands there with a vacuous grin on his face, and just parrots the same old phrases again and again, about being "modern", "moving on" and "drawing a line" under things!

Well that's probably enough about our pitiful little would-be preacher. The best thing we can all do with that sort of person is draw a line and move on!

Yours,

St Albion's Man Of The Week

CONGRATULATIONS to Mr Byers for having the decency and honesty to admit that he had done nothing wrong when he told a lie to the PCC!

If only all our parishioners could be as courageous as Stephen in admitting they have done nothing wrong! Food for thought, eh? T.B.

PS. Congratulations also to Mrs Hewitt, who has now admitted that she did nothing wrong in giving an important parish appointment to a woman, even though a much better-qualified man was available. I adopted exactly the same policy when I appointed Mrs Hewitt! T.B.

Parish Transport

Dr Reid Writes:

Some people have been complaining about the vicar's wife driving around St Albion in a tank paid for out of parish funds.

Get real! We live in a violent world and there are a lot of people who have got it in for the vicar's wife. £2 billion is a small price to pay for the knowledge that Cherie can pop out to the shops to buy a free dress without putting her life at risk.

So let's hear no more about this supposed "luxury tank" and I would warn any whingers to keep out of her way, as they may find themselves being run over by a very heavy armoured vehicle.

Get my drift, Jimmy?!

CALLING ALL DADS!!

Great news for fathers! *(writes Mr Blunkett).* Our new plan for giving all fathers time off to look after their newborn children is proving hugely popular. We have long since moved on from the days when mums could be expected to stay at home looking after their little ones, thus wasting their valuable workplace skills. Now dads will be free to play their proper part, as mothers to their children, instead of wasting their valuable parenting skills sitting round in the workplace. And, guess what? The Vicar is right behind our new scheme! Only the other day, he said to me, "Six months paternity leave with each child? I rather doubt whether we'll ever see you at work again, David!"

Nice one, Tony! D.B.

NEWS FROM ACROSS THE POND!

The head of our mission overseas, Mr Straw, has been on an extended evangelical visit to Sister Condi's Alabama Crusade. As you all know, Sister Condi is a leading light in Reverend Dubya's Church of the Latter-Day Morons and she could be the first female black Moron to lead the Tabernacle!

So what a good thing that Jack has spent so much time there joining in prayer, breaking bread and banging the tambourine along to such gospel favourites as 'Shall We Bomb Them By The River', 'When The Troops Go Marching In' and 'Glory, Glory, Alledubya'.

This is a much better use of Jack's time than hanging around in the parish, going to meetings and doing his job. T.B.

Jack and Condi with some children!! Says Mr Straw, "Don't worry, they are not mine. They're Blunkett's".

Hullo!

Or, as I had to say to my good friend Mr Blunkett, "goodbye", when, very sadly, he told me that he was going to resign from the PCC.

Let's be quite clear. David did nothing wrong! I'll go further. I'd like to put on record here and now that David is the finest, most upright, most principled, most decent human being it has ever been my privilege to meet on this earth (apart, of course, from myself!).

I hear that some people in the parish are going round saying, "The Vicar's lost his grip and the parish is falling apart". (OK, Mr Marshall-Andrews, I know who you are! Sitting in the bar at the Britannia Arms, drinking round the clock – which, incidentally, you've got me to thank for!)

Well, for your information, I'm not losing my grip in any way whatsoever! And the proof of that is as follows:

● Would someone who was losing their grip twice ask Mr Blunkett to stay on, despite the embarrassment that would ensue? No!

● Would someone losing his grip be pressing on with all his plans for modernising the entire infrastructure of St Albion's, including the launch of the new Walmart-Kwikfit St Albion's Foundation Hospital, Primary School and Personal Finance Centre? Not much grip-losing there, is there?

● Would someone losing their grip be given no fewer than 18 designer watches from Father Silvio Berlusconi, the head of the much-respected Church of the Cosa Nostra in Palermo? I think not!

No, I tell you what I've lost. It's not my grip, I've lost. It is the services of my most decent, loyal, trustworthy and hard-working friend, Mr Blunkett.

A man whose unimpeachable integrity shines before all of us to guide us on the true path that leads to salvation. (Or rehabilitation, as we call it now!)

I wonder how many of the children can remember that story from the Bible about the scapegoat?

No, Tariq, it's not the new film with Wallace and Gromit. Yes, Asbo, I know you'd much rather be watching that than listening to me!

But let me tell you anyway! The scapegoat was an entirely

innocent bearded creature who, for no reason, was driven out and stoned to death by members of the tabloid press.

Isn't that a really horrid story, children? Just imagine that poor old goat, who'd done nothing wrong, having to resign from the rest of the goat community, just because, as the Good Book tells us, there was "not a stain of impropriety upon that goat of many colours"

The vicar unveils a new statue in the churchyard. As seen by our local artist Mr de la Nougerede.

(Letter of Timothy Rice to the Thespians).

And, I'm quoting that story completely from memory! So, hey, who's lost their grip?

That goat was "Whiter than white", exactly as I prophesied it would be, as long ago as 1997!

So it was never "many-coloured" at all, as certain people keep claiming! Are you still with me, children?

Which brings me to my seventh point. Some old-fashioned people still cling to some very out-dated notions, such as that it is what they used to call "sinful" ("unhelpful", as we would call it today) for members of the PCC to buy and sell shares!

How mad can you get? And I'm the one who is supposed to be losing my grip! Pur-lease! As if! Whatever!

(If you wish to show your support for the vicar, text him now on 077077 or contact the vicarage website on www.stillvicar.com)

And, to my third and most important point of all. People are apparently saying that I am turning into my predecessor, the Rev. Major, by clinging onto my job while everyone around me is getting up to sleazy practices!

Well, all I can say is that, as I said to my wife Norman at breakfast, I am not inconsiderably incandescent at this suggestion, which is in my judgement in no small measure the work of BASTARDS who I have put in my book, oh yes!

Yours,

Tony Major (age 52¾)

—Salve—

Welcome to Mr Hutton, who has taken Mr Blunkett's place on the PCC. Most of you won't have heard of Mr Hutton or think he is the charming old gentleman who wrote that splendid report saying that Mr Campbell and I had done nothing wrong over the sad death of our local GP, Dr Kelly! He is not that Mr Hutton, but it doesn't matter because he is also a very loyal supporter of everything I have done since coming to the parish, and that's the main thing, isn't it? T.B.

✉ Parish Postbag

Mr Blunkett's Letter To The Vicar

Dear Tony,

Although, as you know, I have never done anything wrong, after our little talk this morning I could smell and feel that it would be a good idea if I was to step down from the PCC.

It has been a great privilege for you to have me as a valued part of your team, and I feel sure that you will soon want to have me back, as you did last time!

With heartfelt thanks,
Your best friend,
David
PS. Sadie sends her love!

MEDIA HIGHLIGHTS

Many of you may have missed a very interesting programme on Saturday on St Albion's Foundation Hospital Radio. The vicar made a surprise guest appearance on "Football Focus" and was asked to choose his "Dream Team". The newsletter is delighted to reprint it in full!

Tony's Dream Footy XV

Jonny
Wilkinson

Freddie   Ellen   Frankie   Bob
Flintoff   McArthur   Dettori   Geldof

Alan   Ruth   Hazel
Milburn   Kelly   Blears

Alastair   Rev.   David   Frank
Campbell   Blair   Beckham   Bruno
(captain)

Sub: Dame Kelly Holmes

As you can see, Tony knows just as much about football as he does about running St Albion's!! Ed.

ST ALBION PARISH NEWS

25th November 2005

Hullo,

You all know the phrase "more in sorrow than anger"?

Well, I'm writing to you this week more in anger than in sorrow!

And you don't have to have a GCSE Grade A* in rocket science to know why!

When I recently asked the congregation to give its views on Mr Clarke's new Neighbourhood Watch plans for the parish, you collectively chose to reject them.

Now, don't get me wrong! You are of course fully entitled to do that. There's no law against it (or not yet, although Mr Clarke tells me he's working on it!).

But I'm equally entitled to feel a little bit aggrieved that you've all chosen to disagree with me, even though I'm right!

Can I quote some words of scripture here, because I think you'll agree that they are pretty relevant to the situation here in St Albion's.

"It is a far, far better thing to do the right thing and lose, than to do the wrong thing and be on the winning side." (*Temptations of St Anthony, 7.4*).

But we don't have to get all heavy with scripture (which was written a long time ago, and we've all moved on from that, haven't we?) to see the point on this one.

I am sure you all remember that great film Twelve Angry Men, starring Jane Fonda's father.

And do you remember that, to begin with, there's only one man who is right, and all the others are completely wrong, thanks to their prejudice and stupidity!

But the hero of the film (played by Tony Fonda) refuses to back down, because he just knows that he's right!

And gradually, one by one, they all come round to his point of view and plead with him, with tears in their eyes, to stay on as vicar!

Then they all gather round the Christmas tree and sing "For He's a Jolly Good Vicar"! Isn't that a wonderful ending – and one that I think has got a message for all of us (or should I say, for all of you?).

And this brings me to my third point, which was that it wasn't only me who was right about the Neighbourhood Watch. I know every member of the PCC received a personal letter from our local chief policeman, Inspector Blair (no relation), asking them to support me.

I've even got a copy of his letter here which I am printing in full below, just in case any of you think I am making it up!

Dear PCC Member,
I am writing to you personally on a very important matter. The vicar has asked me to do this in my capacity as the most senior policeman in St Albion's and as a completely independent expert on why you should support the vicar's proposals that your policemen should have the power to lock everyone up in order to find out who they are and whether they have done anything wrong.
Yours sincerely,
Inspector I. Blair MA (Oxon).
PS. As you can see from the envelope, I know where you live! You see, we policemen aren't all thick plods, as you snobby middle-class people seem to think!

So, there you have it, from a totally independent source – proof that I am right and everyone not called Blair is wrong!
Yours,

Kookery Korner

with the Rev. Dubya of the Church of the Latter-Day Morons

This week:
Shake 'n' Bake

1. Take one tub of best quality Texan plain white phosphorus.

2. Shake well, serve up and just watch 'em bake!

This is an old Southern recipe passed on to me by a good friend of the Bush family, old Ma Cheney! As she likes to say, "It was a favourite for the nigras, and now it goes down just as well with Iraquoons!"

✉ Parish Postbag

Dear Sir,

I was rudely asked recently to attend a PCC sub-committee meeting looking into the way the parish is run. I have no intention of being quizzed about my activities by a lot of ignorant parishioners. A very important person like myself has more pressing things to do, such as looking out of the window to see if the sky is still blue.

Yours far too busy to write letters,
J. Birt,
Attic Flat, The Vicarage.

The Editor writes: Letters from Mr Birt will not be cut due to his being a personal friend of the Vicar.

Dear Sir,

I am totally disgustivated by Mr Christopher Meyer's discalled for remarks about the Vicar and indeed myself in his new so-called book. What a toffee-nosed prat!

To suggestify that I cannot even excess myself properly is completely pretosteros.... presumpterous... prosperitous... fooking wrong!

Yours,
J. Prescott,
C/o Working Men's Club.

 *Women's Groups*

*O*UR THANKS to the vicar's wife, who gave us yet another of her fascinating talks, this time on "the benefits of a university education". Mrs Blair told us that if she hadn't been lucky enough to go to a university, she might well have ended up as nothing more than "a dreary little shop girl". How we all laughed at the thought of the First Lady of the Parish standing behind a counter selling things, instead of standing in front of it and being given them all for free!

Mrs Blair then graciously took questions from the audience, and inevitably was asked about the success of her fascinating book "Life Behind The Scenes at The Vicarage". Mrs Blair emphasised that she had never taken advantage of her position as the vicar's wife, except when she had!

Refreshments were provided by Mrs Blears, who because it was still Ramadan, handed everyone an empty plate!

ST ALBION PARISH NEWS

9th December 2005

Hullo!

And this is the time of year when our thoughts turn to the less fortunate members of our community, particularly, of course, the elderly.

And, you know, I often think that one of my greatest privileges as your vicar is to be able to help old people in a very real way.

That's why I asked Mr Turner, one of our local businessmen, to spend a couple of years looking long and hard at how best we can assist our senior parishioners to enjoy the twilight of their lives.

Well, Mr Turner has finally come up with his 8,000-page report, which is available on the table in the porch, and I do strongly urge you to spend a few moments reading it on your way out of church.

Mr Turner really has done a marvellous job, and I am sure that in due course we shall be acting on every one of his excellent suggestions.

His main suggestion is that, with all of us living much longer these days, the so-called 'twilight' period of our lives should begin much later, some time between 75 and 100.

Hey, that makes sense, doesn't it?

Another of Mr Turner's very good ideas is that lots of people don't want to retire and spend the rest of their lives gardening, playing golf and going on cruises to the fjords.

No, they want to carry on working as long as they can, making a useful contribution to society, by taking satisfying part-time manual work, such as digging coal, mending the roads or stacking the shelves in Tesco.

Do you remember those wonderful words of St Paul in his *Letters to the Liverpudlians*: "Will you still need me, will you still feed me, when I'm 64?"

Well, we certainly will – except, of course, that we won't have to feed you any more because you'll all have one of Mr Turner's Britsaver pension schemes, and anyway who thinks of 64 as being old nowadays?

I'm sure that if St Paul was still with us today, he would be only too happy to support Mr Turner by changing the words of his famous epistle to "when I'm 94"!

So, it's great stuff from Mr Turner! A message of real hope, compassion and goodwill, at this season of Christmas/Hanukkah/ Diwali/Sudoku or whatever you have chosen to believe in this year!

So, what a pity that one or two people (well, one to be precise) have chosen to adopt a thoroughly negative and unhelpful attitude to Mr Turner's admirable proposals!

I don't want to name names (but I think our Treasurer may know who I'm talking about!) when I refer to the person who couldn't even wait for the report to be placed in the porch before announcing to anyone who was prepared to listen that Mr Turner didn't know what he was talking about.

"How can we afford it?" says our Scottish friend, who thinks these proposals of Mr Turner's are just pie-in-the-sky!

Does such a response remind us of another famous Christmas character?

No, not Father Christmas – he's the one who believes in giving at Christmas, not taking away!

I am thinking of a mean and miserly old Caledonian gentleman, who sits all day and all night counting his money (and usually getting it wrong!).

Yes, it's our old friend from Charles Dickens, Ebenezer Scrooge!

And we all know what happened to him in the Good Book, don't we?

He got his comeuppance, didn't he, when he burst into flames and was reduced to a pile of ashes?

Of course, no one is suggesting that anything like that is going to happen to Mr Brown, although might it not be quite appropriate if it did? There's something for us all to pray for during this Advent (from the Greek 'ad-ventos', meaning 'a calendar full of chocolates')!

One thing Mr Turner didn't get round to considering was the case of someone who, although still relatively young, has been stuck in the same job for many years, and would benefit from immediate early retirement. Perhaps to a remote island off the coast of his native Scotland! No offence, Gordon, but how does that old hymn go again – "Will ye no come back again – please"?!!!

Yours,

Tony

St Albion's Primary School

Mrs Kelly writes: Next term we are going to introduce a new idea, which I am sure all parents will want to know about! It is called READING. Children are shown words in a book, and are told how to "read" them. Does it sound complicated? It's actually very easy, and children soon get the hang of it! So let's all give it a go, shall we, and if you have any problems or queries, please don't write to me or come to see me, because I am a very busy person. R.K.

 Parish Postbag

Dear Sir,

*I was shocked, as I am sure were all other parishioners, by the unhelpful comments of the Parish Treasurer in relation to our (well, **my!**) European Mission. It is quite wrong for Mr Brown to criticise the vicar over his supposed lack of commitment to Europe when we all know that Gordon is **much** more of a eurosceptic at heart and anyway is simply trying to undermine the vicar in a silly bitchy way. It is just like all these people who are trying to make trouble for me over my partner Rinaldo and the immigration status of his charming friend Brazilio da Novisa! Honestly, some people have a cheek!*

Yours absolutely livid,
P. Mandelson,
Rue des Matelots, Bruxelles

KEEPY UPPY!

A sad picture of a middle-aged man trying to play football! Another own goal, I'm afraid, Gordon!!! T.B.

Thought For The Day

In Favour of Temperance

The sad death of George Best is a reminder to us all of the perils of over-indulgence in alcohol. I do not have to look far in my own family circle to find an example of a man who was once a great talent, but who succumbed to the demon drink. I'm thinking of my poor father-in-law Tony Booze who has begun to rant and rave about me, suggesting that I am not up to the job as vicar! I am sure it is just the drink talking but, even so, it is a tragic state of affairs. Perhaps, now that Tony Booze has moved to Ireland, he won't come back and, like poor George Best, will be laid to rest beneath the emerald sod. May he rest in peace. T.B.

TV CORNER!

If anyone missed the Vicar's wife's wonderful new TV programme "I am a Golfish" about life in the vicarage, they will be able to obtain a DVD of the broadcast at a modest price of £27.99p. In fact even if you did see it, you will obviously want to see it again! And indeed we insist you do.

So anyone who fails to order a DVD of this wonderful insight into the life of goldfish will be visited by Mr Campbell and asked to explain why.

WARNING: He knows where you live.

This is a recent photograph of a boy in the parish who is going round pretending to be me – even ordering cups of tea to try and persuade people that he is the vicar! If you see this boy, can you please report him to the local Neighbourhood Watch before he breaks into the vicarage and takes over! T.B.

ST ALBION PARISH NEWS

25th December 2005

By popular demand (!), the newsletter is delighted to reproduce the Vicar's Christmas Day Sermon in full. Enjoy!!

Blɔɔ!

And a very happy Wintervali to you all!

This is the Season of Renewal, and I know you will all want to know my personal resolution for the year which lies ahead!

Well, that's an easy one! Even the children could get that one!

No, Tariq, I am not going to resign. Quite the opposite!

My resolution is that I am going to stay on as your vicar and finish the job!

It's what I call my "legacy".

It's a big word that comes from the Greek "Legassos", something that is completely forgotten.

So don't let anyone tell you that I've come to the end of my time here at St Albion's.

Particularly, I would suggest, that moon-faced young man who had the cheek to interrupt my sermon the other day, by shouting out to the entire congregation, "you were the future once, but now you're the past it"!

What nonsense! I could easily have come up with some devastating put-down that would have shut him up for good.

But, hey, that's not my style! I thought it would be much more effective if I just stood there with my mouth open and said nothing!

And so it proved! Our young friend was made to look very foolish, as you could see from the way everyone laughed and waved their hymn sheets!

Which reminds me of my other New Year's resolution which I've just thought of.

I am not going to waste my time going on about young Mr Cameron, who is a silly boy who's got nothing better to do than go round the parish drinking cups of tea and smiling at everyone!

How pathetic! He won't get very far doing that, will he?

The answer is "no, he won't", thank you, Sayonara, not "it hasn't done you any harm".

Perhaps Mrs Kelly could make sure that in future you attend our Special Needs Sunday Club!

Anyway, I expect you all remember that story about the rich

young man in the Bible who wanted to do good in the world, even though he'd been to Eton!

And what was he told? He was told, politely but firmly, to go away and leave that kind of thing to those who really know what they are doing!

And that young man went away sadly, and was never heard of again!

And, my goodness me, isn't there a lesson there for certain soppy young men in this parish today?

I don't want to go on about him, but really! Why does he have to bring his wife into everything all the time, cuddling up to her whenever there's anyone with a camera phone nearby?

As I said to Cherie, this is not the kind of thing she and I would do!

In fact she's given me a quote for this newsletter, which I am delighted to put in.

This is what she said: *"If you need a last-minute Christmas present idea, why not purchase a copy of "I am a goldfish: Life inside The Vicarage" by Cherie Booth and Melvina Barg. £12.99. Three-for-the-price-of-one at Waterstone's."*

Thank you, Cherie!

Which brings me to my sixth and final point, as we go forward into 2006.

I have absolutely no plans to retire. But, when I do, I have no wish whatever just to slink away to the St Albion's Sunset Home for Rich Friends of The Vicar, and sit there reminiscing about how much better things used to be when I was the vicar instead of Mr Brown, or rather more likely that soppy boy whose name I'm never going to mention again.

A Happy Chinese New Year to you all. And guess what? It's the Year of the Vicar!

© *T. Blair, 2005*

Thanks!!!

Thanks for nothing to Mr Blunkett who is telling everyone that I've got it wrong about my plans to turn St Albion's Infant School into the Kwik-Fit Beacon Academy. Well, I've learnt one lesson already and that's not to expect gratitude from someone whose career you've saved twice!

No wonder you can't find anyone to have your babies, David, when you treat your closest friend so shabbily!

Shame on you, David, and Happy Christmas! T.B.

We hereby publish the Banns of Gay Marriage between Peter, a spin-ster of this parish (!), now of Le Quartier des Matelots, Bruxelles and Rinaldo formerly a bachelor of the Parish of Los Amigos de Dorothea, Rio de Janeiro. This is for the 49th time of asking so get on with it Peter!!

If anyone know of any just cause or impediment why these two may not be joined in Civil Partnership they are to keep quiet about it because Mr. Mandelson is a personal friend of the Vicar. Ok? T.B.

Thought For The Day

We hear a lot about '"Free speech" don't we, but there are limits, as there are to everything in life. There is a limit to how fast we can go in our cars, a limit to how long you can park in the church car park and a limit to my patience with silly women who stand outside the vicarage gate reading out the names of people for whose deaths I am mysteriously responsible!!

Well what would you do if someone did that to you in the middle of the night – or day, as it was in this case? Obviously you would call the police and get Maya Evans put in prison as a terrorist which is clearly what she is.

So let's hear no more about "freedom of speech". What about "freedom from deranged women reading out names of dead people"?

That's surely a more important freedom, isn't it? T.B.

A Christmas Prayer

To remember in your prayers: Mr Kennedy, Moderator of the United Reformed Liberal Democrat Church.

Mr Kennedy is under a great deal of pressure from his congregation and is being urged to stand down and give way to a better-qualified older man. It is always sad when a church leader loses the confidence of his flock and let us all pray that Mr Kennedy sets an example to us all by staying on, even though he is obviously ill equipped to do the job with which he has been entrusted – probably because of a weakness for all things scotch, if you know what I mean! Cheers! *Amen* T.B.

—Valete—

It's goodbye to Mr Birt who has occupied the office in the vicarage attic for the last few years. As you know, Mr Birt has been busy doing "Blue Sky Thinking".

And what he has been thinking is that he would like to earn a great deal of money! So he has decided to join local millionaire Mr Guy Handout in his exciting company Terra Firma. So you see, Mr Birt has gone from "Blue Sky" to "Terra Firma" and now his feet are *firmly* on the ground!!

We wish him well and would like to thank him for all his "input" (great word, John!), which has turned the Parish into a thriving resource module rolled out across all the parameters of the outsourced intranet market paradigm. *(Is that right, John?)* Tony Blair.

Hullo,

And firstly, can Cherie and I thank you very much for all those wonderful Christmas cards which we found pushed through the door when we got back from our little "winter break" in the Holy Land (or a beach quite nearby!).

I was sorry to see that there had obviously been a bit of a mix-up by whoever was responsible for choosing one of the two cards, because instead of the traditional seasonal message, it read "Wishing you well in your retirement".

Since it was signed by the entire congregation, I was rather surprised that no one had noticed – but I am sure you all meant well!

At least the other card, from Tesco, managed to get the traditional message right – i.e. "Tesco's Two-for-One Turkey Offer – Hurry, hurry while Christmas lasts!".

But enough of the festive season and all that goodwill, Christmas 2005 is actually one I would be very happy to forget.

As you may remember, I had to go over to Brussels before Christmas for a meeting of the Oecumenical Union Council (for which, incidentally, yours truly was "President").

And guess what happened? Talk about predictable!

As soon as we'd finished our lunch, our French friend Monsignor Chirac called for the bill and handed it to me, saying to the entire table in that pompous way he has, "We're all agreed that Rev. Blair should pay for everyone".

This was exactly what he said last time! And I repeated what I said before – that it was completely unfair that my parishioners should be expected to fork out for all the vast quantity of food that everyone round the table – all twenty-five of them – had consumed!

Monsignor Chirac, as usual, didn't stint himself at all, as he munched his way through the following items, viz:

> 12 kilograms snails in garlic butter
> 158 "jambes de grenouille" (whatever they are!)
> 16 lobster thermidors, stuffed with foie gras
> 1 trolley full of assorted cheeses (French only)
> 1300 profiteroles.

And if that wasn't enough, you should have seen what the new woman pastor from Germany managed to tuck away! Frau Merkel managed to make her predecessor Pastor Schroeder look as though he was on a diet.

It would be unfair to go into detail, but suffice to say that at one point it looked as though Brussels was going to run out of sausages and sauerkraut entirely!

Anyway, when it came to the bill, I had to point out that I had made a solemn pledge to my parishioners that I would not agree to spend a single extra penny from the parish funds on providing free lunches for our continental colleagues!

Then Monsignor Chirac had the audacity to point down to the bottom of the table where the Polish, Slovakian and Latvian ministers were putting the cutlery in their pockets and say that they had only come to the lunch on the condition that Rev. Blair paid for everything.

"You are surely not expecting these poor people to pay for their own rollmop herrings and rye bread?" said M. Chirac, pretending to be all caring and compassionate to our eastern European friends (as he ordered another bottle of vintage Chateau Lafraud claret for himself).

Well, naturally, I was not going to put up with this cheap blackmail for a second!

When I have given my word to my parishioners on something, I stick to it!

Do you remember my predecessor, Deaconess Thatcher, used to say all those years ago; "The vicar's not for turning" (*Book of Rebates, 19. 84*)?

Well, let me tell you, I'm a lot tougher than she ever was! And when it comes to "not turning", I can "not turn" just as firmly as she ever could!

That is why I refused to turn, right up to the end, and it was only at the very last minute when the whole table was shouting at me, that I finally agreed to pay the bill!

But I only agreed to do so on one condition: that Monsignor Chirac should think very seriously about possibly reducing his intake at our meals by asking for slightly less food than is his wont – e.g. perhaps one or two fewer snails!

When he saw how determined I was, Monsignor Chirac immediately caved in with a broad smile, and agreed to all my demands.

"Of course, mon cher Antoine, I will think about your proposition very carefully indeed!"

Only seconds later, he said "I have now thought about it, and the answer is 'non'".

Everyone round the table laughed sympathetically, to cover his embarrassment at the fact that he had been made to look a bit of a fool by my tough negotiating skills!

Yours,

Tony

A Plea to Parishioners!!!

The church "Bring and Buy" committee has asked members of the congregation not to hand in any more copies of *My Life As A Goldfish: Inside The Vicarage* by Mrs Cherie Booth Q.C. and Melvina Barg. Of course it is a brilliant book, but we already have several hundred second-hand copies contributed by generous parishioners, and the books are not selling quite as quickly as we would have liked. T.B.

The Legal Beagle!

Local solicitor Mr Falconer writes:

There seems to be some misunderstanding about the Parish Policy with regard to Freedom of Information. Of course you are free to write in with whatever silly questions you care to ask about how St Albion is run. That's democracy! But what a lot of you don't understand is that I am also free not to tell you anything if I do not want to. That's also democracy!

So let's hear no more about this silly idea. C.F.

This Year's Best Christmas Cracker Joke!

Q: Why is the vicar like a Christmas fairy?

A: Because every year he ends up "top of the tree"!

(Thanks for that one, sent in by Mrs Blears. Well spotted, Hazel!)

✝ To Remember In Your Prayers

● All those loyal servants of St Albion who have generously donated large sums of money to the vicar but have yet to be honoured by the parish due to a few envious and bitter members of the PCC. May these sour and uncharitable miseries remember the Biblical parable of the rich men who got into heaven immediately through the eye of the needle by giving Jesus lots of money. Q.E.D!! T.B.

Mr Brown's New Year Resolution
(as suggested by the vicar!!)

I MUST BE MORE PATIENT!!

As seen by local artist Mr de la Nougerede

A MESSAGE FROM MR PRESCOTT, DEPUTY CHAIRMAN OF THE PCC

LISTEN. I am extremely disenheartened by the negative respondences to my Parish Building Initiatives: i.e. the poncey middle-class so-called "country-lovers" who whinge every time I suggest putting a few thousand houses on the churchyard, the kiddies recreation ground or the parish cricket field (only a game for toffs and nancy boys, in my view).

Let me make it abundantly clear that we need every available metre of space in this parish to provide much-needed housing stock for our rapidly growing population of asylum seekers, divorced parents and old folk living on their own. These are the groups whose needs must be urgently prioritivated rather than effete toffee-nosed middle-class tossers (if you'll forgive my French!), bleating on about how wonderful the view used to be from their so-called patios and conservatoires before we were fortunate enough to get the new Tesco extension at the bottom of their gardens.

And while I'm on about poncey middle-class boogers (forgive my Slovakian!), can I just say that the vicar's plans to turn our local Herbert Morrison Comprehensive into the PC World St Albion Technology Beacon Academy are just plain daft, and that soppy lass he's got in tow, Mrs Kelly, could do with a bit of proper educatering in the "school of life", if you ask me, which I know Tony won't because, frankly

Sadly the editor has had to cut the rest of this ranting and disloyal tirade for reasons of space (and also because Mr Prescott is extremely lucky to have a job at all, and was only kept there because the vicar needed to appoint someone from the Working Men's Club to make it look as if...

The Vicar regrets that he has had to cut the editor's comments for reasons of space. T.B.

ST ALBION PARISH NEWS

20th January 2006

Hullo,

And what a great start to the New Year we are having, with the launch of my new 'Respect' campaign!

I am sure every one of you will now be familiar with what I am hoping to achieve for the parish with this 'Respect Action Plan'! And yes, kids, have you noticed what that spells out? Yes, R-A-P!! Or 'Rap'!

You can't get much more modern, young and with-it than that, can you?

If there is one thing which everyone in this parish must be agreed on, it's that we're all just sick and tired of the 'yob culture' – young people who spend their time littering the streets, swigging lager, defacing public buildings, urinating in the bus shelter, spitting at old ladies and listening to violent and mindless 'rap' music on their iPods!

Well, I'm not just going to talk about 'Respect'! I'm going to do something about it, and that's why I've come up with an 84-page 'Action Plan' (available on the vicarage website, www. respectthevicar.com) that we can all think about and discuss over the next few months.

In it I spell out a few of my ideas of how we can try to recover some of those old values that our society used to have – not that in any way I want us to go back to some 'mythical golden age' where people went round showing respect to one another and helping old ladies across the road without spitting at them!

No, as you remember, our St Albion's motto is 'Forwards not backwards'! So instead of constantly harking back to the past, let's move forwards, shall we, to a new golden age, where people go round helping old ladies across the road, like they used to do in the old days!

"But vicar," I can hear our friend in Tesco's saying to me, as he queues up at the '10 Items Or Less' checkout with his pathetic wire-basket full of 'Meals For One For The Price Of Two', "haven't we heard all this before? Didn't you preach about the need for 'Respect' back in 1997, and then again in 1998 and 1999 and every year since?"

Well, yes, actually, and I don't mind admitting that I did! And you know why? Because it was important then, and it's important now!

So let's have a little more 'respect', particularly from embittered malcontents in Tesco's who seem to have nothing better to do with their sad and empty lives but try and find new excuses for criticising your vicar!

Which brings me neatly to my fourth and final point, which is about annoying neighbours who try to make life difficult for decent, ordinary, hard-working folk!

Why should we put up with neighbours like these, with their squealing babies, their temper tantrums and the constant noise of their computers bleeping away day and night because they can't get the parish accounts to add up properly!

The last straw comes when these neighbours start hanging out dirty great union flags from the bedroom and start singing "Rule Britannia" at all hours of the day and night!!

Under my new proposals, such 'neighbours from hell' will be evicted and sent back to Scotland where they belong!

It may sound harsh, but sometimes, as it says in the good book, "You have to be cruel to be kind" (*Book of Asbos, 15. 17*).

Think about it!

Yours 'respectfully',

Tony

The vicar and his friends show their 'Respect' for Mr Campbell, the elderly acting leader of the United Reformed Liberal Democrat Church. As seen by Mr de la Nougerede.

IDENTI-TEA CRISIS!

May I just remind parishioners that the young man in this photograph is NOT, repeat NOT the Vicar! It is sad to see a promising young man suffering from serious delusions such as thinking that merely by drinking tea he can be a vicar! Look, *I* was the first person to drink tea round here and it is rather pathetic to see other people trying to steal my tea idea – what you might call jumping on the tea-wagon!! Tea.B. (!)

Parish Postbag

Dear Sir,

I was surprised to read in the St Albion's Clarion that 'Mr Brown had done a first class job with the parish finances'. Without wishing to disparage a former close colleague, I have to say that the view from Brussels is rather different! I would not go so far as to say that Mr Brown has made a complete pig's ear of everything but will confine myself to saying merely that a child of six could have done a better job than this over-rated bungler!

Yours,
P. Mandelson (former churchwarden),
Rue des Matelots, Bruxelles.

Editor's note: For reasons of space all letters attacking Mr Brown will be printed in full.

A STATEMENT FROM MR PRESCOTT, OF THE WORKING MEN'S CLUB

I would like to clarificate my position on the small matter of my failure to pay the council tax due on my free flat (kindly provided by the parish) above the Working Men's Club.

Of course I had every intention of rebursurating the trifling sum of £460,000 which had accruated over the last ten years, but due to an unfortunate oversight which I sadly managed to repeat every year, the bill was never paid.

In any case, it is pathetic that people have created such a fuss over such a pilfering matter when there are important issues to be dealt with, ie thousands of cunning old ladies trying to avoid long-term imprisonment by wilfully defying the laws of the land by not paying their council tax. Shame on you grannies, you deserve "a poonch in the kisser" and no mistake!

Yours,
J. Prescott,
The Primary Residence,
Grace and Favour House,
Freebie Lane,
SW1 ZZZ

New Blue Plaque in Parish

(*Thanks to local artist Mr Latham for this one!*)

ST ALBION PARISH NEWS

3rd February 2006

Hullo,

And I don't mind admitting that it's a bit lonely up here on the highwire!

Because, as I keep saying, that's where I am – walking a tightrope, with plenty of people down below, hoping that I'll fall off! It's at a time like this that you realise who your real friends are! And I can tell you that as of now it seems like I haven't got any!

As I look down from my high wire (no safety net – this is the real thing!) I can see all those people who I thought were my friends looking up and shouting, "go on vicar, fall off and break your neck!". Not very nice, is it? And these are people who only got where they are today thanks to me!

OK, one expects the likes of Mr Marshall-Andrews to make trouble. Haven't we all of us had to put up with the spectacle of him sitting there on Sunday mornings at the back of the congregation, shouting 'looney' during my sermons!

It's no surprise that he can't see the point of my plans to turn our local primary school into a Wal-Mart Beacon of Excellence Starter Academy of Retail Technology and the Performing Arts!

But when I am being criticised by the likes of Mrs Estelle Morris, then, frankly, I feel like jumping down off my wire and strangling her with my bare hands! (I don't obviously, I'm only talking figuratively, in the Biblical sense, but I am sure you will all know what I mean!)

Has Mrs Morris forgotten how many times I had to step in to save her skin when she was the headmistress of the primary school? Honestly, she makes Mrs Kelly look almost competent. (No offence, Ruth, just my little joke – we all know that it wasn't your fault that you appointed St Albion's best-known flasher to be the lollipop man – anyone could have made that mistake, except me, of course, which is why I'm the one who's up here on the high wire, while the rest of you are down there whingeing and trying to make me fall off!)

And who's that bald old man who is shouting up at me in Welsh? I am sure few people in the parish will remember him, but it was me who gave Mr Kinnock a helping hand when he was down and out, and found him a part-time job and accommodation in the Old People's Home.

Look, I'm not asking Neil for gratitude, but at least he could say 'thank you'!

Instead of which he's telling me that I'm wrong about everything (well, from your own past record, you'd certainly know all about that, wouldn't you? No offence, Neil, but you are in danger of becoming something of a whingeing Welsh windbag!).

And, as for the Judas of them all, what about Mr Alastair 'Iscariot' Campbell, the former editor of this newsletter!

The Vicar on a highwire
(Thanks to Mr de la N!)

Alastair might like to remember that when I dragged him out of the gutter he was no more than a foul-mouthed drunk who'd had a nervous breakdown! It was me who turned him into a foul-mouthed drunk who edited this newsletter!

What's more, we even gave a job to his partner Fiona, who used to run errands for Cherie and help with the typing!

It's a bit much to see those two getting on their high horse and telling me how to run the parish!

As it says in the Good Book; "with friends like those, who needs enemies, puh-leese?" (*Book of Ruth Kelly, 17.4*).

Look don't get me wrong. I've got nothing against people such as Alastair, Fiona, Neil and all the other traitors contributing to a free and open debate about things they know nothing about!

But let me tell you something. From where I'm standing, up here in the hot seat on the high wire, my best friend – and I know this is going to come as a shock to most of you – seems to be that silly boy David Cameron, who's been going round the parish drinking tea and pretending to be the vicar!

Do you remember the story in the Bible about the very rich young man from Eton who asks Our Lord what he has to do to enter the 'kingdom of heaven'?

And Our Lord replied, "Give away all that you believe in and copy me". (You'll find it in the *Sermon Given To Ferdinand Mount*, as one of what we call 'the Pleatitudes', along with 'Blessed are the Warmakers' and all those other great sayings!).

Doesn't that make you all feel ashamed?

Which brings me to my fifth and final point – i.e. what a nerve Mr Prescott of the Working Men's Club has got trying to tell me about education!

All I can say is that if I want advice about education, I'll ask someone who can read and write! (No offence, John, but it's not spelled with a 'sh' in the middle either!)

Yours (still up in the air!),

Tony

CONGRATULATIONS!

To Mr and Mrs Brown on their forthcoming happy event (no, Gordon – you'll have to wait more than 9 months for that one!). It's just a shame that Gordon feels he has to copy the vicar's idea about having children later in life – particularly when you are not as fit as the vicar. To be frank, you might have better things to do with your evenings, such as try and balance the books which are in such a terrible mess! No offence!

And talking of pale imitations, I could not help noticing this picture of Gordon copying my tea idea in the hope of making people think he is the vicar. Nice try, Gordon – but here's a PG-Tip! Why not try and balance the parish accounts instead. T.B.

SQUATTERS

I have received a number of complaints about the unemployed disabled man who is currently squatting in Grace and Favour House behind the vicarage.

Surely our message should be one of compassion and tolerance for poor Mr Blunkett who, through entirely his own fault, finds himself in this very cushy number. T.B.

Parishioners Reunited

A column that keeps you posted on Albionians, old and new!

Congratulations to Mr Birt who you remember used to sit in the attic in the vicarage looking out of the window at the blue skies and trying to think of something important.

At last John has found a job equal to his talents, advising businessmen how to ring up the vicarage and say "I'm a friend of John's".

If you have any Albionian news, do write in! As Mr Birt always says, "Keep in touch, you know it makes money!".

Keep fit with Mrs Hewitt!

Hello everyone! Just to let you know that there is a new voluntary compulsory keep fit class!

Starting next month every single member of the parish will be given their own personal trainer and a check-up or MOT(!!) on their state of health. This is a wonderful opportunity to keep us all in tip-top condition as well as rooting out the scroungers, smokers, drinkers, fatsos and all the other deadwood that the rest of us are having to pay for!!

The Mobile Fitness Detector Van will be visiting your area soon. Pat Hewitt.

ST ALBION PARISH NEWS
17th February 2006

Hullo!

And I think the first thing we all need to do this week is to calm down, take a few deep breaths and count to ten (and the kids of today can count to ten, I'm happy to say, whatever some people might like to claim!).

In the last few days, voices have been raised in anger, tempers have frayed, a few extremists have had a field day – and we now need to take stock and think very carefully about where we go from here.

People have shouted at me from the back of the church, calling me an "idiot" and a "lunatic".

Mr Kinnock, who was a lay reader here in the 1980s (and, I have to say, a rather unpopular and unsuccessful one at that, although it would be uncharitable to point this out!) has even suggested that I should resign!

Well, he's perfectly entitled to think that and to make his views known to all and sundry!

Hey, that's what it's all about! If we believe in anything, we surely all believe in the free and frank exchange of views and in people's rights to make their opinions known, however stupid and ignorant they may be!

I respect their right to speak out. But they in turn must respect my right to ignore them! How could I possibly continue to run this parish if, every time I want to do something, we all have to sit for hours around a table, discussing whether it is a good idea or not?

Dear me, if we operated like that, nothing would ever get done at all!

No, when you appointed me as your vicar, you didn't appoint Mr Kinnock, did you?

Look, we all believe in freedom of speech. We all need to respect the points of view of other people, even if we disagree with them.

We all need to practise restraint, tolerance and open-mindedness in what could otherwise become a very dangerous and ugly debate.

I'm talking, of course, about all those who have questioned my latest plans to turn St Albion's School into a Kwikfit Selective Independent Beacon Academy.

Now some of you have expressed your views about this in rather a negative and extreme way.

You didn't appoint Mr Marshall-Andrews or Mrs Morris, did you – let alone Mr Prescott?!

All of which leads me to my sixth and final point. I am listening to your views, and I'm taking on board all that you have said! And that isn't a sign of weakness! Quite the contrary! It's a sign of strength!

As it says in the Good Book, "The tree that bends in the wind is stronger than the reed that snaps" (*Book of Aesop, 4.94*).

So, to sum it up, our new Academy will not be selective, or independent, or a beacon, or sponsored by Kwikfit.

But apart from that, the plans will be exactly as I said they would be all along!

I couldn't put it any simpler than that, could I?

So, let's put an end to this so-called "clash of cultures" that threatens to destroy the civilised world of St Albion's as we know it!

> Yours, walking the line,
> "The Man In Black"
>
> Tony

NEXT WEEK'S SERMON will be given by our guest preacher Ayatollah Imamad Bastardi on the text "Kill Thy Neighbour As Thyself".

The vicar's suggestions for changes to the church tower! As seen by Mr de la Nougerede.

A Message From Mr Brown

Hello,

And welcome to my message which from now on will be getting equal billing with the Vicar's! As you can see, I've been trying on the vestments and guess what...? They fit me perfectly! Some might say, they fit even better than they do the Vicar!

I just wanted to alert everyone to a series of addresses I shall be giving during Lent (or Borrowed, as I call it!). I shall be in the church on weekdays (8.30am-10pm), talking on the following subjects:

Monday: *Where are we going?*
Tuesday: *What is the future?*
Wednesday: *The way forward*
Thursday: *No turning back*
Friday: *Facing tomorrow*
Saturday: *The challenge ahead*

Of course, on Sunday, you will still have to listen to the Vicar – but not for long! We all admire him for the hard work he has put in over the last eight years – but it has to be said, he has left a lot for his successor to do.

And, for the record, the Vicar's suggestion in the last newsletter that I have taken up drinking tea in order to copy what he calls his "Big Tea Idea" ("The Third Cup" and all that) is absolute rubbish. I was drinking tea years before he was and, let's be honest, if anyone is likely to be stealing ideas, it's him. No offence, Tony, as you would say!

The Almost Reverend Gordon Brown
(Church of Scotland), Lay Preacher and Vicar-In-Waiting

Sadly there will not be room for this excellent new feature in any future newsletters due to pressure of space. This is a great shame as it was such an amusing read! T.B.

MYSTERY!!

The Vicar writes:
I have had a Valentine card containing the following very lovely message:

Roses are red,
Violets are blue,
There's only one
*   person left*
Who still loves you!
Mrs H. Blears

I wonder who could have sent it? T.B.

WANTED

Former PCC member, now unemployed, seeks accommodation, but not very hard. In fact, not at all. If you know of a flat or house suitable for Mr Blunkett and his dog, do not contact him, as he is more than happy living for free in Grace And Favour Road.

Women's Groups

*O*ur speaker next month is none other than one of the country's best-known lawyers, Mrs Cherie Booth QC. As one of our leading experts on human rights, she will be talking about "The right to wear a wig and make a huge amount of money". Tickets at £20 each (no concessions) are sure to be in demand, so book early. Talk sponsored by the St Albion's "Friends of the Taliban".

This week's recipe comes from Mrs Kelly

CHUCKED EGG

1. Take one egg.
2. Break carefully over my head.

(Serves no purpose at all)

ST ALBION PARISH NEWS
3rd March 2006

Hullo!

And if there is one thing which the modern church stands for more than anything else, it is the need to stamp out the "sin" (or social evil, as we call it nowadays) of smoking. So let's do it!

In fact, for once, I think the word "sin" is really quite relevant when you think how many millions of people in the parish are now dying every day as the result of the selfish actions of a tiny minority!

It is only when we are confronted with what my friend and mentor the Rev. Dubya of the Church of the Latter-Day Morons so rightly calls "evilitude", that we come to a new understanding of all those old teachings about the wages of sin being death!

And doesn't it say in the Good Book, "thou shalt not smoke" as the first commandment? (*Book of Deutyfree 7.12*).

No beating about the bush there! No little sub-clauses about smoking being OK in the Working Men's Club, or in the Britannia Arms, so long as they are only serving pork scratchings!

I know Mrs Hewitt and Dr Reid may have given some people the impression that some kind of compromise might be acceptable.

And I know dear old Jock Reid got misty-eyed about the thought of his old comrades back in Glasgow being deprived of their only source of pleasure, as they huddle together for warmth in the bar over a pint of whisky!

Goodness me, we've moved on from those days, Jock! And a good thing too!

No, to ask for any compromise on this, the most centrally important moral issue of our time (apart of course from the sin of fox-hunting!) is like asking for a compromise on any of the other commandments!

You can't say "Thou shalt not kill", but it's perfectly alright to go and do it in another country, like Iraq or Afghanistan.

It's like saying, "Thou shalt not commit adultery, unless you are a member of the PCC like Mr Blunkett"!

All of which brings me to my fifth point, which is the difficulty some people seem to be having over the meaning of the word "glorification".

I really can't understand why there should be any confusion over this word.

Look at it this way, if we really admire someone and think they're really good at their job, and that everything they do is brilliant – which it may be! – then it's only right and proper that we should "glorify" them! In other words, give them the "glorification", which is their due.

So, what's important is that you should learn to glorify the right people and things, and not to glorify the wrong people and the wrong things!

Hey, I know it's a long word – and I wouldn't bank on Mr Prescott getting very far with it! – but really it's very simple!

I've even written a chorus for next Sunday's evening service:

Glor-if-i-cation, glor-if-i-cation!
Sing it out across the nation!
Praise our vicar to the sky,
Glory, glory, glor-ify!

Yours in glory!

Tony

Design for a splendid new stained-glass window. Many thanks to local artist Mr de la Nougerede

On sale in the Vestry Bookshop

How to Sue the Vicar by Cherie Booth Q.C. (£915.99)

Cherie's latest book explains in easy-to-follow legal language (and a mere 994 pages!) just how you can extract large sums of money from the PCC by suing them for compensation. *(Do you really want me to put this in? T.B.) (Yes, I bloody well do, and I'll sue you if you don't! C.B.)*

✝ To Remember In Your Prayers

● Poor Mr Marshall-Andrews, who has got into yet another fight with an innocent parishioner. I know that Mr Marshall-Andrews and I have had our differences, but it is always sad to see any fellow human being falling prey to an insatiable craving for alcohol. It is obviously too late for poor wino Bob to derive any benefit from a visit to AA or, indeed, a course in anger-management! So I'm sure you will all want to pray for a speedy release for this sick individual from his mortal suffering. I am sure when Bob reaches 'the other side' that he and Mrs Mowlam will have a lot to discuss! T.B.

Question and Answer with Mr Prescott

Q: Why are you building 170 new houses on St Albion's recreation ground when there is a hosepipe ban in the parish?

A: Due to globalised-warming there is a droughtification situation in the parish as of the current time. However the warmingisation of the globe will result in the meltdown of all the ice up north which will flood the south and we will have as much water as we want.

Q: Won't the houses then be flooded?

A: Shut up, ya pasty-faced southern tosser or you'll get a smack in the kisser. I'm bloody John Prescott me.

Next week: A chance to put your questions to Mr Campbell who will tell you to fuck off because he knows where you live. T.B.

ST ALBION PARISH NEWS

17th March 2006

Hullo,

And I know a lot of you will have been listening at 6 o'clock in the morning last week to Mike Parkinson's very popular show on St Albion's Hospital Radio, 'Hi there bedblockers!'. As you will have noticed, it was a pretty tough interview, as it always is with Mike!

He really puts you through your paces, and you have to be on your toes, remembering all your best anecdotes and jokes!

But many of you have been kind enough to email and text the vicarage, to tell me that I was pretty brilliant, and that if ever I'm out of a job (which I won't be, Gordon, so don't get too excited!) then I could walk straight into Mike's seat in the studio!

For those of you who didn't hear it, the highlight of the show had to be when Mike asked me what was my favourite colour!

This was a perfect cue for me to explain why I thought I would be proved right in everything I have preached about our great crusade against the Evil One in Iraq.

I hope you don't mind if I quote myself here, but it would be difficult to put it better!

TONY: *"Hey it's not up to me to judge whether I'm right or not. I leave that to history and to God, and frankly, I'm pretty confident I know what both of them are going to say!*

You remember that famous quote from the Good Book 'Well done, thou good and faithful servant'? (Justifications, 9.11).

Well, I'm not saying that those will be the exact words which greet me on Judgement Day, but I wouldn't mind betting that they will be pretty similar!"

Anyway, you can see that the point I was trying to make was that it's not up to human beings to judge something as important as our Great Crusade against what the Rev. Dubya likes to call the 'terrorification of eviltude'.

And that particularly includes all those parishioners of St Albion who have been far too quick to 'play God', by passing judgement on me themselves.

Look, it's not a picnic doing this job as the vicar of the parish. You have to take tough decisions, such as whether or not to support the Rev. Dubya and the Church of the Latter-Day Morons – and decisions like that don't come easy!

No wonder Sister Condy has to get up at 4 o'clock in the morning, to do her exercises and meditation in preparation for the hard day ahead!

I myself have had many sleepless nights, wrestling with my conscience about whether to answer the telephone when I know it's going to be the Rev. Dubya ringing up to ask if I've said my prayers!

Don't get me wrong! I in no way resent the fact that I've probably got the hardest job in the world!

All I'm saying to those who wish to criticise is that,

frankly, it's none of their business, and they should leave it to the experts, i.e. God, to decide that everything I've done was right after all!

Yours,

God   *(Is this right? Ed.)*

Thought For The Week

THE FLIGHT OUT OF BRITAIN INTO EGYPT

"Render unto Dubya those people which are Dubya's"
(Book of Renditions, 7.3)

Let's all take these words to heart and stop criticising the Vicar for following this commandment, shall we? T.B.

Their Special Day!!

The vicar was delighted to officiate at the special Service of Temporary Separation for his good friend Mrs Jowell and Mr Mills. In his moving address, Tony said that untying the knot was always a difficult decision to make, and it wasn't to be entered into lightly. He wanted to commend Tessa and David for the mature and civilised way in which they had come to their decision, motivated only by a desire to save the vicar any embarrassment and to enable Tessa to keep her job in charge of the new casino in the vestry. The vicar spoke briefly on the unimportance of holy matrimony in the modern era, and said he felt sure that the unhappy couple would soon be reunited once the dust had settled and we had all moved on.

The vicar read from the Epistle to the Roman Prosecuting Magistrates, including the famous text 'Greater love hath no woman than this: she should lay down her husband for her job'.

At a reception in the vicarage afterwards, tea and refreshments were served by the Matrons of Dishonour – Mrs Beckett, Mrs Jay and Mrs Blears. The Separation cake was ceremonially cut by Mrs Jowell (who was delighted to find inside it a file on her husband compiled by the Serious Fraud Office!).

Tessa leads the congregation in an impromptu sing-song on the vicarage lawn. Everyone joined in for that rousing hymn by St Tammy of Wynette: 'Don't Stand by Your Man'!

ST ALBION PARISH NEWS

31st March 2006

Hullo!

Or should I say "Goodbye" – because I know that's what some of you want to hear me say!

No names, but I am sure the entire parish will know who I am referring to – ie them!

Well, by way of an answer, can I just quote those immortal words from the Good Book, 'no way, Hosé' (*Book of Hosé-a, 4.16*).

No, this storm in a teacup, which is all it is, frankly, has been blown up out of all proportion by a tiny minority of a few hundred thousand misguided individuals whose sole aim in life is to stir up trouble and make life difficult for the vicar!

What they're saying is that I've secretly been lent money – small sums of millions of pounds – by a number of charitably-disposed local businessmen, whose only aim is to further the work I've been trying to do in the parish (with very little thanks, I might say!).

And yet their names have been dragged through the mud and gossiped about in the Britannia Arms, just as if they were common criminals who were only in it for themselves!

Honestly! Let's look at these people, shall we?

● Mr Gulag Loon, proprietor of the New Mumbai Star Curry House in the High Street (Balti and Tandoori dishes a speciality).

● Dr Bakhanda Patel, proprietor of our much-admired Farewell Home For The Elderly, in Laburnum Crescent.

● Mr Rob Allbust, who runs "Mr Megabyte", the computer repair shop next to Tesco and opposite the other Tesco (just before you get to the Tesco Metro Corner Shop, but not as far as our new out-of-town Tesco Supastore).

● Mr Barry Townspiv, our much-respected independent financial adviser, who runs the Fillyerbootz One-Stop-Stock-Shop from above the chip shop.

I could go on! But who could read this list of some of the most distinguished wealth-creators in the parish without coming to the conclusion that you could not want a straighter bunch of guys, whose only concern is to serve the needs of our St Albion's community in any way they can?

Let's look again, for example, at the contribution of Mr Loon.

Who amongst us has not waited patiently at the counter for one of his delicious chicken tikka massala takeaways, with extra pappadums and a carton of cucumber raita?

This is the kind of man we're talking about here, a real pillar of the community!

Or consider Mr Patel, whose only aim is to help our old folk to die with dignity as quickly and painlessly as possible. What more admirable contribution could anyone make to the life of our parish?

And Mr Townspiv, giving his time to advising young and old alike on the best way to maximise their hard-earned savings by investing in the mysterious world of the Stock Market.

As it happens, I know all these men myself, because I was introduced to them at the St Albion's Tennis Club by my friend Mr Levy who, as you know, has been my tennis partner for many years.

And if these generous guys want to lend a few bob to help me out in my mission here in St Albion's, then surely it's no one's business except theirs?

Hey, *I've* got nothing to hide – but *they* didn't want everyone to know how generous they'd been, because they are so modest!

So naturally, I didn't go round shouting about it to people like Mr Brown, Mr Prescott and Mr Dromey, our parish book-keeper.

I'm not saying they can't be trusted! But I couldn't be absolutely sure that they wouldn't go around the parish blabbing their mouths off and pretending there was something dodgy about my borrowing all this money on the quiet from men who run curry houses and computer shops!

So there we are! I did nothing wrong and nor did anybody else – except Mr Brown, Mr Prescott and Mr Dromey, obviously!

But then that's the kind of betrayal I've come to expect in this job. It goes with the territory!

And just in case some of you are still concerned about what has happened, let me assure you that every penny I've borrowed will be carefully accounted for, and that our whole system of financing the parish will be completely reformed, root and branch, so that none of these disgraceful things can ever happen again!

As for these so-called businessmen, who have been trying to use their ill-gotten gains to "curry favour" (got it, Mr Loon?) and win influence in the parish, let me make it clear that they will not be getting any favours from me, and they certainly won't be getting any of their money back, because we've spent it all on our exciting campaign putting up a poster in the Tesco car park with the brilliant slogan "Support Your Vicar – We Know Where You Live".

Yours in the red *(surely "the Lord"? Ed.)*,

Tony

✚ To Remember In Your Prayers

● Mr and Mrs Dromey (better known to us all as Mrs Harman and her ghastly 'partner' who used to have a beard). In the light of Mr Dromey's recent unfortunate outburst about the vicar, let us pray that Harriet will have the wisdom to follow the fine moral example set by Mrs Jowell and will arrange for her marriage to break down as soon as possible. T.B.

This Week's 'Words of Comfort'

"It is easier for a rich man to enter the kingdom than a poor man, because he's got more money." *St Luke Johnson, 7.23*

"It is better to lend than to give, because then it doesn't show up in the accounts." *Book of Levy, 12.1*

"Blessed are the rich, for they shall dwell in the House of the Lords forever." *Book of the Prophet Margin, 14.16*

WE'RE SORRY!

The Parish Accounts

We're sorry, but there just isn't enough room to print Mr Brown the Treasurer's report in full. Suffice it to say, that contrary to all the nonsense that everybody is talking around the parish, his handling of the finances has in no way been exceptional, brilliant or marvellous. Also, his presentation in front of the PCC was, to be honest, a little embarrassing. Those awful jokes! That terrible tie! No offence, Gordon, but as they say in the European Song Contest, "Nul points" from the vicarage!

I mean, since when have you been interested in sport, Gordon, or indeed any form of exercise? (No offence, mate, but you could lose a few pounds and I don't mean the type that keep disappearing in the parish accounts!)

Look, there isn't space, as I said, to go on and on about this, but all that long-winded guff about education. Yes, we know you've suddenly got children, Gordon. Yawn! So, where did you get that idea then...?! The same place you got the drinking-tea-all-the-time idea!!! ie, ME AGAIN!!

So, if you seriously want to be vicar one day, Gordon, you really will have to try a great deal harder. I'm not going to use the word "lacklustre" about your performance because, to be honest, it wasn't that good.

● For a full point-by-point analysis of Mr Brown's presentation, go to the vicar's blog at www.revblog.co.uk

Welcome!

We are much looking forward to this Sunday's Evening Service, which will be taken by Mr Straw's sister, Suzy Shaw (known as "Cloud Dancer"), who is the High Priestess of our local Gaian Fellowship. Suzy will lead the congregation in a celebration of healing, dance and "hot stone rituals", and parishioners are asked to come in loose-fitting clothes and sandals.

Mr Straw writes: *This is nothing to do with me, and sadly I shall be unable to attend, owing to the fact that I shall be on a mission to Iraq where, despite the civil war, everything is going extremely well.*

OOPS!!

When, in an interview last year on St Albion's Cottage Hospital Radio, I said that I was considering retirement, many of you may have got the impression that I was considering retirement.

Well, hey – here's a first – and I'm big enough to admit it – I may have been wrong!?!!

Of course what I meant was that Gordon is going to retire soon and that I shall be here serving you as your Vicar for all eternity – "I am with you always." *(Book of Common Errors 1599 – or £13.99 in the Vestry Bookshop!)* T.B.

ST ALBION PARISH NEWS

14th April 2006

Hullo!

And let me say at once I'm really sick of being told that I'm 'having a row with Gordon'. As you all know, Gordon and I go back a long way and we've been working together, singing from the same hymn sheet, for many, many, many years – and I'll tell you what, that's the way it is going to stay. Me and Gordon. Gordon and me. Shoulder to shoulder. How did that old hymn have it? "Walking along, singing a song, side by side" (*Hymns Modern and Modern*), So there you have it. No rift. No row. No split. Just a couple of old pals doing what they do best. Getting along. Singing a song. Side by side. Except, of course, with Gordon just a little bit behind!

But, as with all relationships, there are bound to be times when we don't get along quite as well as normal, times when we have a few minor disagreements. That's bound to happen, particularly when one of the partners is a difficult person to like, someone who always wants to call the shots and tends to get in a sulk if he doesn't get his own way. I'm not necessarily saying that Gordon is like that – but of course we all know that he is. As Mr Byers and Mr Milburn have been explaining to as many parishioners as they can find who will listen, which alas is not nearly enough since they both sadly had to resign from the PCC under something of a cloud which was, of course, not in any way of their making... er... where was I?

All of which brings me to my fourth and final point. Despite the fact that I am ***not*** having a row with Gordon, it has become only too evident that when it comes to the job he is meant to be doing i.e. looking after the parish accounts, he has been found hopelessly inadequate. If I was ***not*** having a row with him I might have had to take him to one side and say something pretty cross to him. Like, "For goodness sake, Gordon, pull your socks up or I'll have to find someone who can add up to do your job!"

And then people would have said, "Look, the vicar and the treasurer are having a row!" Which of course we are not.

Which leads naturally to my fifth point, which is Gordon's ridiculous idea that he might one day succeed me as the vicar. Oh dear! I wonder who put that idea into his head? Just because we had dinner at a restaurant a very, very long time ago that's no excuse for Gordon to get ideas above his station.

And just because I *may* have mentioned a date to him as a time when I *might* think of retiring, it doesn't mean I have any intention of retiring now or at any time in the future!

And how could I? Cherie was kind enough to give me a ten-year diary for Christmas and it is already chock-a-block with important engagements for every week right up to Christmas 2016. And just look at some of the things which I've got to do.

● March 14th 2007: Open the new Tesco in Tesco Road.

● June 10th 2008: Get Mrs Beckett to paint over the graffiti on the Millennium Tent.

● September 28th 2009: Abolish poverty.

● February 11th 2010: Cut waiting lists at St Albion's hospital by closing it down.

● February 9th 2011: Ditto St Albion's Kwik-Fit Beacon Technology Primary School.

● July 20th 2012: Attend opening ceremony of the Reverend Tony Blair memorial Olympic-style games in the Tesco carpark.

● September 7th 2012: Appear on St Albion's Community hospital radio to choose my favourite records.

And that's only a few of the millions of important things that I've agreed to do in the next 10 years!

And you'll note it wasn't Gordon they asked to these events but yours truly. After all, who would want to hear some grumpy old Scotsman on the radio playing his favourite bagpipe tunes when they could be listening to *me* and Mick Jagger?!

But hey, don't any of you go away with the idea that Gordon and I are not really great mates! We go back a long way, we've been working together for many, many years etc, etc. And here's the proof – how can two people have a row when they are not even talking to each other? Think about it!

Yours,

Tony

"I'll be there for you" *(Book of Friends, Ch. 7.13)*, as seen by Mr de la Nougerede

LOCAL MEDIA ALERT

Since the vicar, Mr Brown, Mr Prescott and the rest of the PCC are at present very busy with pressing parish affairs, the vicar wants it to be known that Mrs Beckett will be answering all your enquiries about everything until further notice: e.g. the row Gordon and I are not having; why Mr Sainsbury was quite right not to tell anyone that he 'lent' the Parish £2 million in exchange for being given a seat on the PCC; and why she is the only person the vicar can trust not to say something stupid! T.B.

Announcements

Well done, Gordon, for your mission this week to go and be photographed with Saint Nelson of Mandela. I hate to quibble with such a noble and generous gesture (with the parish's money, mind you!), but, hey, haven't we seen this idea somewhere before? Let me give you a clue: The tea-drinking idea? The having-a-baby idea? Does this ring a bell?

No offence, Gordon, but isn't it time that you started thinking up some ideas for yourself instead of copying everything I do! T.B.

Parish Postbag

Dear Sir,

How often do we have to hear these pathetic stories about the vicar and Mr Brown not getting on? I know Tony and Gordon better than anyone else in the world and, take it from me, they are the best friends that anyone could ever be. *Is this the sort of thing you wanted me to say, Tony? It should annoy Gordon anyway!*

Yours faithfully,

P. Mandelson,
Rue des Matelots,
Avenue de la Constitution,
Bruxelles.

PS. Je sais où vous habitez!

✟ To Remember In Your Prayers

● Mr Mills, rather better known to most of us as Mrs Jowell's husband. Let us pray that, having sneaked back into the parish hoping that nobody would notice, Mr Mills may be given the wisdom to return to Italy again as soon as possible, and meanwhile to keep his big mouth shut! May he come to learn that it doesn't help anyone for him to go round telling everyone that he only left Tessa to "take the heat off her" and that it would not be long now before they were back together again! May he remember that if he happens to be wondering what to do with the odd £350,000 'present' that he might have been given by my friend Silvio, then we are rather short of money ourselves at the moment and we could use it to repay a few of our 'fairweather friends' who've now suddenly decided that they want their money back. T.B.

St Albion's Welcomes Sister Condi

Mr Straw writes: I can't tell you how excited I was when my special friend, the beautiful Sister Condi of the Church of the Latter-Day Morons graciously agreed to pay a three-day visit to St Albion's, just to see me! And I was allowed to be her personal escort the whole time she was here! I thought very carefully about what such a beautiful and distinguished nun might want to see, and long before she'd arrived I'd got our itinerary all sorted out (not to mention my new contact lenses, to make me look younger and more handsome!).

We began when I met her at the bus station and she stepped out of her coach and I told her that she looked like a million dollars in her beautifully cut Moron suit and high heels! I thought to myself, "What a shame that this vision of loveliness should have dedicated her life to the service of the Rev. Dubya, when she might have made some lucky man a perfect partner!" Our three days went by like I was in a dream. Did we really have that unforgettable dance together in the St Albion's Youth Club, to the sound of the Beatles singing 'She Loves Me, Yeah, Yeah, Yeah'? And did we really have a candlelit pint of beer in the Frog and Firkin as the Karaoke machine played 'I Wanna Hold Your Hand'! She flashed me one of her lovely smiles and said it was one of the most romantic places she'd ever been to! And did we really pay a visit together to our local mosque? No we didn't, because there was a huge crowd standing in the street outside telling her to go home! J.S.

ST ALBION PARISH NEWS

28th April 2006

Hullo *(and not, you'll note, "Hullo, hullo, hullo"!),*

Let me make it clear once and for all that I have not been arrested!

Just because a police car was seen outside the vicarage last week, and two police officers came in for a little chat, does not mean that I face a lengthy gaol sentence!

I've heard of people jumping to conclusions but, honestly, how stupid can you get?

Lots of people have police officers round for tea, so why shouldn't your vicar?

Just because they stayed for twelve hours and took away my computer and bank statements, doesn't mean I'm some sort of common criminal, or that they've "got anything on me"!

No, this whole thing is a storm in a teacup, as my friend Mr Levy from the tennis club made absolutely clear when he had the police round for a friendly cup of tea as well!

And, let's be honest, if anyone has questions to answer about recent donations to parish funds, then it's not me, it's Mr Levy.

Goodness me, I can't do everything here! I know some people think I'm superhuman, but I can't be on duty 24/7, can I?

I have to delegate some things to other people, and, frankly,

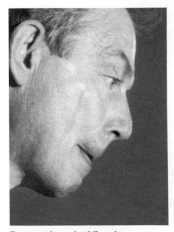

Remember the Vicar's manifesto promise? "Perspiration, perspiration, perspiration"!

arranging much-needed loans from local businessmen is very much one of them – as is finding people who are generous enough to sponsor the St Albion's Beacon Academy of Business Studies Excellence (formerly the Herbert Morrison Comprehensive).

And talking of how busy I am trying to do everything else around here, it's no surprise that I occasionally break into a bit of sweat!

It doesn't mean, I hasten to add, that I'm sweating because the police are after me because of what Mr Levy and those businessmen have been up to!

Not at all! And anyway, I wasn't sweating. It was a very hot day, and

I had just come in from the rain!

So naturally there was a little bit of moisture pouring down my face, and it was nothing whatever to do with being worried about going to gaol for a long time – because that's what Mr Levy is going to be doing, if anyone goes to prison, which of course they're not going to!

And, anyway, if anyone still thinks that I've got something to hide about this business, then perhaps they should listen to the independent opinion of my friend Mr Falconer, our parish solicitor, who is a very expert lawyer.

As he said in a written statement to some police officers who came round to see him for tea, "The vicar is entirely innocent of all charges, as am I, and we have at all times acted in good faith. It is now time to move on."

Yours in the clear,

Tony

The Collection is now being supervised by some new servers!
As seen by local artist Mr de la Nougerede

AN IMPORTANT MESSAGE FROM THE VICAR'S WIFE

I wish to make it clear that the refurbishment of the vicarage
was not some frivolous make-over, as some people have been
trying to suggest, but a long-overdue and much-needed
renovation of the building which stands at the centre of parish
life. As you all know, the vicar and I have to entertain many
important people from the parish, not to mention foreign visitors.
If, for instance, Tony needs to give an audience to the editor of
our local paper *The St Albion Sun*, Miss Rebekah Filth, it is only
right that he should be able to do so in a suitably large room and
sitting on a golden throne. Anyone who thinks that the modest
cost of £2,816,000 for these essential improvements was a misuse
of parish funds should be aware that they run the risk of
receiving a writ of Scandalum Magnatum under Section 25 of the
Human Rights of the Vicar's Wife Act 2006, which prohibits
criticism of the vicar's wife on any grounds whatever.

    Cherie Booth QC
    Makerich Chambers, ('Rights R Us').

Parish Postbag

Dear Sir,

*   I was outraged last week to be compelled to attend a PCC
inquiry into my activities as "Blue Sky" supremo on behalf of the
vicar. I explained at some length that "I was engaged in establishing
a management policy interface across the resource matrix as a
subset of strategic overview development."*

*   Unfortunately, my slow-witted inquisitors seemed quite unable
to grasp what I was talking about, so making the whole exercise a
complete waste of time. Someone of my importance really has got
better things to do than look out the window and talk nonsense (Is
this right? T.B.).*

*   J. Birt,*
*   The Old Lunatic System,*
*   Accenture Road.*

IT'S A SNIP!

Monsieur André is offering his customers a full hair and beauty treatment for a special discount introductory price of only £7,700. Says one satisfied customer, Mrs C.B. of the vicarage, "This is terrific value for money because the parish is paying for me!"

"It'll be the highlights of your week!" says Monsieur André (formerly Sid Boggins of "Salon Pudding Basin", the Railway Arches).

WARNING!

As you may know, I have recently entered into an email debate with Mr Henry Pooter of the St Albion Observer and Advertiser on the subject of whether I am a threat to civil liberties! Whilst recognising that Mr Pooter is at liberty to hold his ridiculous views, I am equally at liberty to point out to him that I know where he lives! T.B.

ST ALBION PARISH NEWS

12th May 2006

Hullo!

And I'm still here, whatever silly letters are sent and however many loonies are wandering about with placards saying "The End Is Nigh". Well, it isn't. And I'm not going anywhere (just in case our friend from Tesco thinks he can get rid of me by voting for the BNP in the PCC elections!).

And what a lot of nonsense we've been hearing in the past few days about "meltdown", "catastrophe" and it being time for me to go! As I said, I'm *not* going, but what I am doing is bringing some new faces into the PCC to give it a fresh appeal and saying goodbye to a few old friends who have come to the end of their service.

Like Mr Clarke of the Neighbourhood Watch. I know I said last week that he was "indispensable" and had "my full support", but, hey! – even vicars can make mistakes, although I didn't in this case and I've decided to let him go! It's what we call "tough love". So, however much we *love* Charles, we can't have foreign rapists and paedophiles roaming around the churchyard at all hours of the day and night.

So, *vale* (that means "you're fired" in Latin) to Charles and *salve* ("you're hired") to Dr Reid. Dr Reid is a familiar face around the parish and has done most of the jobs in the PCC (!!). To each of them he has brought his own style of no-nonsense Scottish brutality!!

But let's not dwell on these minor matters. Surely it's time that we tried to get all this into some kind of perspective? I mean, can we look at the bigger picture?

OK. So the last nine days in the parish have seen a few blips. But, hang on guys, what about the last nine years?

That's three-hundred-and-sixty-five times more blipless days than the number of days when we had blips! And just think what we have achieved in those last nine years!

A Tesco in every street (sometimes even two!). A hospital within 50 miles of where you live that's open for 24 hours a week – every week!

Class sizes at our new Spud-U-Like Catering and Tourism Academy (formerly the Shirley Williams Comprehensive) down to 50 from 20 only a few years ago. Impressive, eh?

And as for all the tittle-tattle about John, I am not going to dignify it with a mention in this newsletter!

What Mr Prescott does in his public life is entirely a matter for him, and it's none of our business what he does in the privacy of his own office!

I feel sorry for all those people in the parish who've got nothing more important to occupy their thoughts than this kind of trivial and prurient gossip!

That's why I've written a new chorus for this week's Evensong, which I want everyone to learn by heart.

 "Nine years have seen the glory of the coming of myself" (Repeat)

(To the tune of The Battle Bus of the Republic)

Words and music T. Blair.

Tony

After the PCC elections, the Vicar played a traditional game of musical chairs!

Words of Comfort From Mrs Jowell

I have been asked to say a few words on behalf of the Vicar because no one else will.

We all of us owe a lot to the Vicar who, for the last 9 years, has transformed the parish from the sleazy, corrupt, crime-ridden, run-down mess that it was before he arrived, to the beacon of parochial excellence that it is today.

Yet, some people are now saying that the Vicar should resign. What kind of loyalty is this to a man to whom we owe everything, especially our jobs?

Just think – if someone else was brought in, some people would lose their jobs and have to pay back their mortgages and might even have to remarry their husbands!

Let us all think twice before we start casting stones at one of the greatest men who has ever put me in charge of the parish raffle, annual concert and sports day!

I.B. writes: Thank you very much, Tessa, for that unsolicited testimonial. It's just what I asked for!

A Message From Our Treasurer Mr Brown

I would like to apologise to parishioners for the fact that I haven't been much in evidence around the parish recently. This has meant that I haven't been able to play a part in the various rather unfortunate developments for which the Vicar and his friends must take full responsibility. But I would like to assure everyone that before long you will be seeing very much more of me, and I will be devoting my energies full-time to clearing up the mess of the last nine years. G.B.

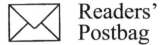 # Readers' Postbag

From Mrs Morris, Mr Raynsford and 94 other Parishioners

Dear Sir,
Whilst in no way wishing to denigrate the Vicar's achievements over the last nine years, we believe that the time has come for him to
> *Yours sincerely,*
> *Mrs Morris, Mr Raynsford and 94 others.*

(Unfortunately, due to the long list of signatories, there was insufficient space to print this letter in full. Our apologies. Editor)

Dear Vicar,
I entirely respect your decision to "let me go" from the PCC, but I would like to put it on the record that in my considered opinion you are a complete
> *Yours sincerely,*
> *Charles Clarke,*
> *The Old Beard Shop,*
> *The High Street.*

(The Editor reserves the right to cut letters for reasons of space.)

Dear Sir,
How dare people criticise our good friend Mr Prescott, who has been subjected to the most disgusting tide of filth I have ever witnessed coming from the likes of the scumbags who now infect our local press. As someone with an unblemished record for upholding standards in the life of this parish, I would like to make it f***ing clear that, when it comes to smearing people up and destroying people's reputations, that is my f***ing job. So, keep out of it, you media tossers, or John will end up having to take his own life like our late GP, Dr Kelly.

Yours insincerely,
A. Campbell, ex-editor of this newsletter.

PS. I enclose my invoice for £47,000 for 'advising' the vicar on PCC matters, which I would like to be paid before his wife's f***ing hairdressing bill, if you don't mind!

ST ALBION PARISH NEWS

26th May 2006

Hullo!

And my apologies if I'm a little brief this week, but I've just got so much to do at the moment that I've hardly got time to write this newsletter!

Unlike some people who seem to have all day to sit around writing stupid articles about me for the local paper!

Not mentioning any names, Mr Clarke! But fancy saying that I had bungled the reshuffle of my new-look PCC, just because when the music stopped there wasn't a chair left for him!

If I did "bungle" anything (which of course I didn't!), it was giving "Dumbo" a job in the first place!

No disrespect, Big-Ears, but you couldn't even shave properly, let alone run the Neighbourhood Watch!

Something even Mr Blunkett could do, and he can't even see! (No disrespect, David!)

But that brings me to all the new initiatives I've launched in the last week alone, to show how incredibly busy I am!

Who says I've run out of ideas, when I've come up with these ten brilliant ideas only this morning?

● Replacing the church's old-fashioned oil-fired boiler with a new state-of-the-art nuclear reactor in the crypt at only four times the cost! And, what's more, it's green!

● All foreigners in the parish to be sent home at once (except of course the ones we're not allowed to deport, which apparently is all of them!).

● The Mission to St Gerry's in Northern Ireland to be reopened, so that we can close it down if it doesn't work! And we won't pay anyone either, unless they agree to work with each other rather than burn down the mission hut as per usual! Somebody's got to bang heads together to stop the violence, and I suppose it'll have to be yours truly! "If you want something done, ask a busy man to do it" (*Book Of Chestnuts 4.16*).

I could go on filling the whole of this newsletter with my new ideas! But I haven't got time to tell you about them all at the moment, because I'm far too busy putting them into practice!

I talk the talk, but I also walk the walk, as my friend the Rev. Dubya of the Church of the Latter-Day Morons once so memorably put it!

And, while I'm on the subject of my new PCC, has anyone made a better start than Mrs Beckett, in her new job as Parish Outreach Co-ordinator, visiting the Rev Dubya in Washington to be told what to do!

Her lovely orange trouser suit really showed the lack of dress sense of poor old Sister Condi, who looked really drab in her black nun's outfit!

I can't imagine what Mr Straw saw in her! In fact, I don't mind admitting that it was lack of judgement that led me to demote him to his new role of putting out the hymn books on Sundays! (No offence, Jack – it's a very important job which I am sure you will do supremely well!)

So, that's all I have time for this week! But just one more thing!

I want to wish our boys all the very best in the World Cup! I shall be supporting them all the way, because I am English – unlike Mr Brown who is, of course, Scottish and has no idea of the meaning of the word "loyalty"! (No offence, Gordon, but leave the football to those who know about it!)

So go out there and score lots of runs, lads!

Yours loyally,

(In the Number 10 Shirt for a long time to come!)

The Vicar absolves Mr Prescott of all his sins (not that he's committed any)! As seen by local artist Mr de la Nougerede.

 Parish Postbag

Dear Vicar,
You specifically asked me to look into corruption in the parish and yet when I deliver my report you
Yours sincerely,
Alastair Graham,
The Sleazefinder General

The Editor reserves the right to cut letters due to reasons of space, especially ones accusing the vicar of corruption. This is common journalistic practice and not at all corrupt. T.B.

Our Core Values
The Vicar writes:

There's been a lot of talk around the parish recently about those "core values" which sum up everything that St Albion's stands for.

When I'm asked, "Vicar, these core values you're always going on about, what are they?" (usually by our friend in Tesco, when he's managed to corner me by the new Polish salted herring, cabbage and sour cream counter), I always reply: "Decency, fairness, tolerance, decency and fairness".

But it's more than this. In fact, for the benefit of all those foreign friends who are so keen to come to live and work in St Albion's, can we try to paint in our mind's eye a picture of all that this parish stands for in our hearts and lives? What about warm beer, cricket, old maids being mugged on their way to evensong, the sound of peerages being bought and sold on a sunny afternoon...

I'm sure all of you will have your own image of all that is best in St Albion's life, which I'd like you to share with me and our parish team, so that we can set in place a "Core Values Template", to be incorporated into the curriculum of our new Al Qaeda Faith Academy (former St Albion's Primary School).

All contributions gratefully received on the vicarage website (when it is back up and running – thanks Accenture!) www.coreval.co.uk

There was a splendid turn-out in the Tesco Parish Hall to see Mr Prescott make his debut as a stand-up comedian. Some of the ladies present might have found the material a little "blue"! But, from his opening joke ("You see they've put me in charge of domestic affairs!") to his sign-off gag ("I'm still very much on the job!"), he had the audience rolling in the aisles, especially when he tried to pretend that he was making a serious speech!! T.B.

ST ALBION PARISH NEWS

9th June 2006

In view of the vicar's absence on one of his many well-deserved holidays, this week's newsletter is written by Mr Prescott (pictured right, by Mr de la Nougerede), who, luckily for us, has enough time on his hands these days to help out with little jobs such as this one. Editor.

BROTHERS!

And that's a word you haven't heard around this parish for rather a considerablised time in my opinion!

And of course when I say "Brothers" I also inclusivise "Sisters" in reference to the female members of the parish, for whom, as is well known, I have a very great respectuality!

And firstly I would like to take this opportunity, with Tony swanning about with his good lady at the Castello Fribi, to clarificate a number of important points with regard to my role in the life of this parish.

Point number one: Contrary to the allegorisations made by a number of disaffectionate individuals, I am still very much the Number Two figure in St Albion's. I am as indispensable as ever, in fact even more so, since it is my job to bang heads together when Gordon and Tony are having one of their poofy tiffs, which you can take it from me is all the bloody time!

If it wasn't for my dipsomatic skills, I can tell you, the whole bloody shooting match would have fallen apart, and we would have become a complete laughing stock!

Point number two: Let me ensure you that I am busier than ever, 23/7, which is why the vicar asked me not to do any of my old jobs any more, so that I could consecrate my energies on the really vital task of knocking balls together on my croquet lawn *(surely "heads together"? Ed.).*

Point number four: Just consider my itinerant for last week:

Monday 4.15pm. Important away-day departmental brainstorming croquet match with key members of the parish team.

Tuesday 11am. Chairing judges' meeting of "St Albion's Largest

Marrow Competition", preparatory to forthcoming annual Flower Show and Fete.

Wednesday 7.15pm. Presiding at ceremonial dinner to launch "Friends of China Society" in our newly-opened Chinese restaurant in the High Street, the Peking Garden, with guest speaker Hang Em Hi from the Chinese Embassy.

Thursday 11am. Important interview with new diary secretary. Shortlist drawn up by Mrs Prescott – includes the following names: Mr Simon Gaytrouser, Mr L.O. Sailor, Mr Mark Oaten.

Friday 9am. Final of departmental think-tank croquet tournament for the Dorneywood Trophy, followed by cebrelatory luncheon at which I proposed a toast to absent friends, ie Tony and Cherie, currently sunning themselves with that little Italian crook they met a few years back who likes to ponce about with a hanky on his head, singing love songs to Cherie and giving Tony watches. It's lucky for them that there's no paparizzas from the St Albion's Sunday Mail snooping around behind a hedge with one of those long-lens digitalised cameras, or heaven knows what the parishioners would think if they knew what their vicar gets up to on his free-loading so-called holidays.

As you will see from the above, I have got my hands well and truly tied (and, no, Mr Mandelson, that is not a double nintendo with reference to Miss Tracy Temple, who has been redeployed to other parish duties under Mr Reid, and, no, that is not another of your double ententes, thank you, Mr Mandelson!).

So, let me surramise, for the benefit of all parishioners what is my message to you this week:

1. I am going nowhere.
2. And if the vicar thinks he can sack me, then he should remember that I know where the bodies are buried.
3. I think I make myself clear, and you can all booger off if you don't like it!

Yours, still very much on the job,
John Prescott,
Horneywood.

P.S. Please note that, as from half an hour ago, all mail items such as letters and cards of sympathy should be forwarded to my old address, c/o the Working Men's Club. I would like to make it clear that my decision to give up my grate-and-flavour residence at Horneywood was entirely my own decision and had nothing to do with the late-night call I received from the vicar, telling me to pack my bags and be out in the morning.

Parish Postbag

Dear Sir,

I have the greatest respect and admiration for John Prescott, who has loyally served the parish for many years, despite his various disadvantages and personal shortcomings. Knowing John as I do, I feel certain that he will wish to do the decent thing as soon as possible.

I enclose a bottle of whisky and a revolver, as a small token of my heartfelt gratitude for our long association, and I am sure he will know how to put them to an appropriate use (if he doesn't try to shoot the whisky and drink the gun, which I wouldn't put past him!).

P. Mandelson,
former Churchwarden,
Rue des Matelots, Bruxelles.

GRAND SUMMER FUND RAISER!!

Your chance to purchase a copy of Dr Kelly's Death Certificate – personally signed by the vicar's wife and Mr Campbell.

Bearing the inscription "Good Riddance, Dr Mitty!" the certificate will be sold by auction to the highest bidder in the vicarage garden at the annual Summer Fete.

Opening bids invited from £2,000!!

Other attractions include: *Guess John Prescott's weight and win a croquet set!* T.B.

A Grave Issue!!

Mrs Harman writes: Following our successful sell-off of half the graveyard for much-needed affordable executive homes, we are now rather short of space for members of the dead community. That is why I have come up with an imaginative new "two for the space of one" burial solution, in which you and your loved ones can be interred in a standing-up situation, just like the famous terracotta warriors of ancient China. This will free up even more space in the churchyard for a new grace-and-favour retirement mansion for Mr Prescott of the Working Men's Club, complete with Olympic-size croquet lawn. Of course, this will only be required in the event of Mr Prescott retiring, which, as he makes clear in the above newsletter, will not be for a very long time yet! H.H.

ST ALBION PARISH NEWS

23rd June 2006

Again, by popular(!) demand, the newsletter is proud to publish the entire text of the Vicar's sermon at the Summer Solstice Service (formerly known as 4th Sunday after Trinity)

And there's obviously only one subject that can be the theme of my message to you all this week.

Can any of the children tell me what that might be?

That's right, Asbo! It's the World Cup!

And isn't it wonderful to have something that draws us all together as one great big family!

Is there anything else which can unite us all as a community – young and old, men and women, black and white, gays and straights, rich and not-quite-so-rich-but-getting-better-off-all-the-time!?

Yes, for a whole month, we can put aside our differences and sit down together in fellowship in front of the big screen.

And, hey, as we're all sitting there sharing our crisps and lager, doesn't that remind us of something? Of a similar sharing-type event involving bread and wine? Think about it!

And here's something else that I want to share with you at this happy time of celebration. Isn't it marvellous to see everyone rallying round and supporting "the team"?

Not sneering from the sidelines, or muttering about the players, but giving 101 percent backing to the guys who represent them!

And above all, of course, they are right behind the most important person on the field – the captain!

Do you see what I'm getting at? The skipper, the leader, the man in charge is rightly looked up to as someone who deserves total respect and loyalty!

Are you getting the picture, everybody? Can you think of someone else who plays a similar role in charge of the "squad"?

Someone else whose name begins with "B"? No, Rashid, not Mr Brown!

I mean someone who's popular, fit, attractive, brim-full of energy, and who has a beautiful, glamorous wife who has a career in her own right and loves to go shopping!

Got it now? Hey, I don't want to press the parallel too far, but wouldn't it be great if *this* captain could expect the same kind of undivided loyalty from his followers as Mr Beckham?

Particularly when he has already won the equivalent of three World Cups!

Not even Mr Beckham can boast that!

And, I don't want to get too personal here, but can I remind you that in all my years leading this parish, I have never once been "sent off" or been caught "playing away".

The vicar captains his winning team! As seen by Mr De La Nougerede

So, wouldn't it be nice to hear the chant echoing round the parish, "Come on, Vicar!"

And, while we are on the theme of the World Cup, can I quote the immortal words of St Kenneth of Wolstenholme – "They think it's all over – but it isn't because the Vicar's still here!".

That should give everyone something to think about while they're watching the football (especially Gordon!).

© *T. Blair, 2005*

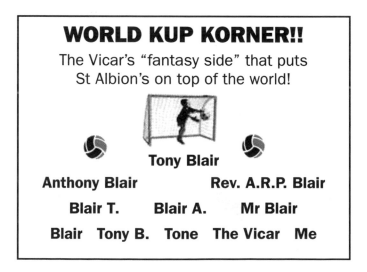

WORLD KUP KORNER!!

The Vicar's "fantasy side" that puts St Albion's on top of the world!

Tony Blair

Anthony Blair   **Rev. A.R.P. Blair**

Blair T.   **Blair A.**   **Mr Blair**

Blair   Tony B.   Tone   The Vicar   Me

CALLING ALL DADS!!!

Mrs Hewitt would like everyone in the parish to read a new leaflet she has produced, entitled "Do's and Don'ts For the Dads of Today", available from the back of the church at only £1 for 100 copies!

Do's

● Do be a 'good Dad' like Tony!

● Do give Mum lots of time for her high-flying career in Malaysia, while you stay at home looking after the baby!

Don'ts

● Don't have affairs with your secretary (like Mr Prescott!).

● Don't have love children (like Mr Blunkett!).

● Don't leave becoming a Dad too late, (like Mr Brown!) or you might end up looking very silly, playing football and listening to the Arctic Monkeys.

● Don't go on about what a great Dad you are because you spend more time with your family nowadays (like Mr Milburn!) because no one will believe you and you're not really as good a Dad as the vicar anyway!

Thanks, Patricia! T.B.

NEIGHBOURHOOD WATCH

Special Amnesty Offer

The PCC is increasingly concerned about the number of knives that are being sharpened and we are very worried about the possibility of a back-stabbing incident later this year. We know who the people are who want to use these knives, but we are willing to offer them a last chance to hand them in before there is any blood on the carpet. So come on, everybody – hand in those knives before someone gets hurt, ie the vicar.

The type of knife that could well be used to stab the vicar in the back ➡

A MESSAGE FROM THE VICAR'S WIFE

There's been a lot of silly gossip around the parish about my recent trip to Malaysia. For the record, I was not told to leave the courtroom. It was entirely my decision to sit outside so that I could hear proceedings better. Nor was I improperly dressed. I just didn't happen to have the right clothes on. Nor do I in any way mind having to forego my £500,000 fee. That was not my reason for visiting Malaysia. My sole purpose in going was to see the countryside and to do some shopping. I would inform anyone who continues to spread these vile and outrageous libels that they will be answerable in the Malaysian Courts – where the penalty for insulting the Vicar's wife is death. You have been warned!

Cherie Booth QC,
The Vicarage.

ST ALBION PARISH NEWS

7th July 2006

Hullo!

I have chosen as my theme this week that very important word 'renewal'.

It's the key to everything I want to do for the parish during my remaining time as your vicar.

What does it mean? Well, let's start off by saying what it doesn't mean.

It certainly doesn't mean changing things just for the sake of changing things!

No. Nor does it necessarily mean that things need to be changed at all!

Nor does it mean that things have to be new!

No way!

How can I explain it? The word is 're-new' – i.e. something that is being made new again!

And doesn't that mean that, in order to be made new again, you have to be old first?

Think of it like your passport. When you 're-new' it (every 10 years), it isn't exactly a new passport, is it?

It may look different. You yourself may look quite a lot older after 10 years (particularly if you've been running a very busy parish with, frankly, not very much help from certain people!).

But essentially your passport is still about you, the same old you that your last one was about.

Except that it has been 'renewed', so that you're all ready for the next 10 years!

Or think of another example. One that we are all familiar with from our church life. I mean 'renewing' your marriage vows.

You don't vow to marry someone else, do you? (Unless of course you are Mr Blunkett or Mr Cook, our late organist, or Mr Prescott, before he got caught!)

No, the whole point of 'renewing' your vows is that you pledge to stay with the same person!

And that is what I want this parish to do – to 'renew' its commitment to supporting its chosen 'partner', in good times or bad times (not that in my case there are any 'bad times'!), in sickness and in health (though there's never been a question about my health, as you will see over the page!).

**Thanks to local artist
Mr de la Nougerede**

As for 'richer' and 'poorer', in this parish, as you know, we've abolished poverty – so the question doesn't arise!

Which brings me to my third point about this important word – the fact that it comes from the Old Greek: 'renos' (staying on) and 'evalos', meaning 'for all eternity'.

Isn't that a message which certain parishioners (particularly the friends of our treasurer Mr Brown) would do well to bear in mind?

What does it say in the Good Book – "I am with you always. And even if the day should come when I am no longer with you, look for me and there I shall be, amongst you"!

And how does it go on? "Behold I am renewed, just as ye shall be also." (*Gospel According To St Anthony*, from the Good Renews Bible.)

And to help you keep these words of wisdom close to your hearts, I've written a special chorus for our Service of Renewal this Sunday.

Renew, renew, renew.
That's what we have to do!
Renewal, renewal, renewal.
Just try it and you'll find you'll
Open up life's door,
And be happy – evermore!
(Repeat)   *Words and music T. Blair.*

Tony

✟ To Remember In Your Prayers

● Mr Clarke, former head of our Neighbourhood Watch, who has recently shown sad signs of galloping mental derangement, no doubt exacerbated by his drinking and his increasing bitterness towards Dr Reid, the new (and much more efficient) head of the Neighbourhood Watch. Let us all pray that Mr Clarke doesn't go downhill even more rapidly, and end up suffering the same tragic fate as Mr Cook and Mrs Mowlam. T.B.

On The Spot With The Vicar!

I send my deepest sympathy to all of our gallant footballing team, but I have a special message for the manager, Sven – why go when there is so much still to be done? Yes, you have a dull sidekick with a Scottish name who wants the top job... but why let him take over when you could carry on and do the job so much better?! It is not too late for you to reconsider your rash decision to step down after losing a few fixtures! I say, "Stay on and 'renew' your legacy of success"!! T.B.

✉ Parish Postbag

A Letter From Mr Prescott of the Working Men's Club

Dear Sir,

Once again, alligators are being made regarding my recent visit to stay on the ranch of Mr Hiram J. Fastbuck of the Las Vegas Wealth Corporation. Mr Fastbuck had generositively agreed to offer me hospitalisation to discuss the possible purchasity of the Millennium Tent prior to its conversion into a 24-hour casino-cum-massage parlour. It was thereforwards perfectly proprietory for me to enjoy the felicities of Mr Fastbuck's hospitality including a delightful massage with

Yours sincerely,

John Prescott, Disgrace and Favour Villas, The Freebie Estate, Croquet Crescent.

The Editor reserves the right to cut any letters for reasons of embarrassment and would like to make it clear that, in return for Mr Fastbuck's offer of accommodation, Mr Prescott gave a donation to charity, which he took out of parish funds. Ed.

Fit For Purpose!

Here's the vicar "running that extra mile" to raise money for one of his favourite good causes – Vicars In Need.

Says Tony, "I am a great believer in physical fitness. It keeps you on the ball and mentally alert. Not like some hopelessly overweight people with big ears and beards! I am not thinking of anyone in particular, but if the cap fits (which it won't, because you've got such big ears), then wear it! Let's be honest, Charles, you let yourself go, which is why in the end I had to let you go!"

And, talking of people who don't look particularly healthy, I rather doubt whether poor Mr Brown could run a mile (though most people would run a mile just to get away from him, especially when he pretends to know about football, or indeed anything else for that matter!).

As for Mr Prescott, can you imagine him taking part in any sport (apart from the obvious one, and no, John, I don't mean croquet!).

A "fat" lot of good he would be at "running" anything (no offence, John!). T.B.

ST ALBION PARISH NEWS

21st July 2006

Hullo!

And not "hullo, hullo, hullo", as our friend from Tesco keeps saying to me, whilst wearing a toy policeman's hat that was given away free with every six-pack of Smarties!

"That is not funny or clever, and you are just a Smarty-Pants!" I said to him, which actually **is** quite funny and clever, even though I say it myself!

" You could be arrested for impersonating a policeman," I went on, as he brought out a plastic truncheon, which had been given away free with a family-size packet of Frosties.

"And you," he replied, "could be arrested for impersonating a vicar."

He then disappeared behind a wall of lager cans bearing the cross of St George, which had been reduced to only 14p per dozen, laughing to himself as though he had said something funny or clever – which, as I said before, he hadn't.

Anyway, it just shows how easy it is for people to get the wrong end of the stick!

As it happens, I would have no problem with meeting members of our local police service, at any time, in any place, to discuss any number of topics they might wish to raise!

I have nothing to hide, and I only wish the same were true of every member of the parish team!

Which brings me to the unfortunate subject of our parish fundraiser, Mr Levy, and the dawn raid on the tennis club.

A lot of people in the parish seem to be under the impression that Mr Levy is in some way a close friend of mine.

Where they got such an idea I cannot think, except it was probably from Mr Levy himself, who has an unfortunate tendency to exaggerate and even to fantasise about his own importance (which may be what got him into his current sad predicament!).

Mr Levy has, I gather, been going round to local businesses, such as the High Noon Curry Emporium or Mr Patel's Friary Clinic For Enormously Rich Drug Addicts and Celebrities, tellling them that, if they hand over large sums of money, he can arrange favours for them from his friend the vicar! All I can say is that if such things ever happened, then certainly I never knew about it!

And if I did know about it, then I would remember it, which I don't!

I naturally feel very sorry for Mr Levy, and will, of course, visit him in prison, because that's what friends are for, as we are instructed to do in the Good Book *(Criminal Acts 9.7)*.

The vicar decides to omit the Confession from the service! As seen by local artist Mr de la Nougerede

But let me make it clear once and for all that Mr Levy is not my friend and never has been.

I only met him once, when we played tennis together, and it was so long ago that I can remember nothing about it, except that Mr Levy made a number of dodgy line calls, which made me think at the time that he was probably not a man to be trusted!

And imagine my surprise later on when he was telling people that he was now leading our mission to the Holy Land!

Well, really! We all know that that's nothing to do with Mr Levy and that the only person whose advice I heed on the Middle East is the Rev. Dubya from the Church of the Latter-Day Morons.

Your friend,

Tony

Bible Stories For Children

No. 94 The Scapegoat – taken from the *Book of Levy*

And in those days in the Holy Land, when someone important was caught out doing wrong, the people chose a goat and drove it out into the wilderness.

And they blamed the goat for all their wrongdoings. And eventually the goat died, which made everyone feel better.

The Vicar writes: What a relevant story this is today! I wonder if any of the children can think of a "goat" who deserves to be cast out into the wilderness today? Someone whose name begins with "L" and who thoroughly deserves all that's coming to him for falsely claiming that he is a friend of the vicar! T.B.

Round And About

We all enjoyed Mr Prescott's recent parish talk in the Millennium Tent (now renamed The Fastbuck Casino). Mr Prescott spoke movingly about the great 19th century reformer William Wilberforce, who set people free to gamble. He told of how poor black people were chained to slot machines in Las Vegas and became even poorer. John was in fine form, and amused everyone by putting on a 10-gallon stetson that he had been given by Mr Fastbuck and pretending to be Clint Eastwood. In keeping with Mr Prescott's "Western" theme *(surely he was meant to be talking about Wilberforce? Ed.)*, the ladies, headed by Mrs Blears and Mrs Kelly, served appropriate refreshments, viz Tex-Mex Tacos, kindly provided by Mr Prescott's friend, Mr Fastbuck. Unfortunately, when it came to question time, Mr Humphrys rather spoiled it for everyone else by asking Mr Prescott several times about his private life and had to be asked to leave. T.B.

PARISH NOTICES

● I will be away next week, as I have been invited to El Porno in California by Mr Murdoch (owner of the Dirty Digger Books, Mags and Vids Warehouse in the High Street). I will be giving a sermon to Mr Murdoch's staff on the text "Blessed are the rich, for it pays to keep in with them" *(Sermon on the Mount of Venus)*.

● I shall also be away next month, taking a well-earned break to "renew" my batteries for the years ahead! (Note the plural, Gordon!! Not year, but years!?!!) Mr Prescott, as usual, will be holding the fort in my absence. But, don't worry, John is a safe pair of hands, so long as he keeps them to himself!! (No offence, John!) T.B.

FROM THE OFFICE OF CHERIE BOOTH QC

There is a vile rumour doing the rounds of the parish that I pulled strings for the husband of my friend Mrs Greed *(surely "Green"? Ed.)*, suggesting that Mr Greed's company, Healthy Profit Plc, should take over the cottage hospital.

Everyone should be warned that I do not intend to take this insult lying down (unlike the people in Mr Greed's hospitals). Anyone who is caught repeating the above slander will be liable to the full majesty of the law and will be issued with a writ of Scandalum Magnatum under the Terrorism Act 2006 and will be liable to be extradited to the state of Texas which, I should remind parishioners, still retains the Death Penalty for serious crimes.

Cherie Booth QC

ST ALBION PARISH NEWS

4th August 2006

Yo!

And let me quickly point out that this is not, as some people seem to think, a disrespectful form of greeting!

On the contrary, the word "yo" is a term of utmost respect and friendship, as used by the Elders of the Church of the Latter-Day Morons!

That is why, when I met my good friend the Rev. Dubya at one of our top-level oecumenical get-togethers in Putingrad (formerly St Petersburg), he went out of his way to use this ancient form of greeting which indicated an equality between brother and brother.

Actually, if you want to know, the word "yo" goes all the way back to one of the noblest of all the Native American tribes, the Iraquois.

This was their ceremonial greeting, used only by the chief of the tribe, Talking Bull, when he was visited by a very important fellow chief whom he recognised as someone of equal standing to himself!

When the distinguished visitor came into his oval-shaped wigwam, Talking Bull would hail him with the words "Yo, Running Scared!" and offer him the traditional "Pipe of War".

So that's *that* one sorted out, thank you very much!

As for the rest of the conversation, which was supposed to have made me look rather foolish – well, all I can say is that you didn't hear the full conversation and how it went on after I had switched the microphone off!

So here, for the benefit of everyone, including our friend in Tesco who keeps shouting "Yo, Vicar!" whenever he sees me waiting at the checkout, is a full transcript of what the Rev. Dubya and I actually said to each other when we sat down to break bread with our colleague Archimandrite R.A.S. Putin:

Rev. Dubya: *OK, Tony, now you've switched that pesky mike off, I can tell you what I really think of you! I really respect and value your advice – more than any other person on this old planet of ours!*

Rev. Blair: *Yo, Dubya, you're too kind!*

Rev. Dubya: *No, seriously, ol' buddy, I can't afford to let you go to all those dangerous places in the Holy Land! Why, if anything were to happen to you, it would be like losing an arm or a leg. It would be like Thanksgiving Day without the turkey!*

Rev. Blair: *Yo and double-yo to that!*

Rev. Dubya: *I tell you what, Tone. We'll send Sister Condi. We can lose **her**. But you, my dear old buddy-boots from England-land, if you were not by my side 24/7, who would tell me what to do?*

And, hey, there was a lot more like this. But, to be honest, I'm a bit embarrassed to put it all in print.

Suffice it to say that, in the eyes of the world's most important spiritual leader, your vicar is a serious "player", and not just some pathetic hanger-on who tries to suck up by giving him presents – although I did give him a Burberry sweater, as it

The Vicar's present from the Rev. Dubya, of the Church of the Latter-Day Morons, was a new dog collar... (as seen by local artist Mr de la Nougerede)

happens, in keeping with the ancient custom whereby one Red Indian chief would offer another a woven blanket as a mark of eternal friendship!

So, I hope "yo all" have now got the picture, and that we'll be hearing no more of this silly tittle-tattle that I am somehow just the Rev. Dubya's poodle, at his beck and call.

I've got to go now, as I think that's him on the phone!

Yo sincerely,

Tony

KIDDIES KORNER

JOKE OF THE WEEK

Q: Why isn't the vicar suffering from the heat?

A: Because he has so many fans!

Thanks Mrs Jowell for that one! T.B.

CONGRATULATIONS!!!

We are all of course overjoyed at our treasurer Mr Brown's latest "happy event" – the arrival of little Hamish McTavish Brown! A lovely Scottish name, Gordon, which I am sure will please all three Scottish members of our congregation! But it won't be easy having two small children at such an advanced age! It's certainly not the time to think about taking on any new responsibilities or changing jobs! Much better to concentrate on looking after young Hamish and his wee brother Angus, rather than spend time fretting about parish business that needn't concern you! T.B.

✝ To Remember In Your Prayers

● Mr Straw, who has been very rude about Mrs Beckett's mission to the Holy Land. We pray that Mr Straw may not be consumed by bitterness and envy of Mrs Beckett, who got his old job at the PCC, and may come to realise that he was really useless and had to be sacked. May Mr Straw's sad mental decline serve as a warning to those who disagree with the Rev. Dubya (of the Church of the Latter-Day Morons) and may his current psychological problems resolve themselves in a swift and painless death. T.B.

Poetry Corner
by the Vicar

IF

If you can keep your job
Whilst all about you are telling you to resign,
If you can ignore all criticism,
Whether from left or right,
If you can go on holiday
When things are getting tough,
Then, my son, you must be the vicar.

This poem was written specially for the vicar's sermon to the Rupert Murdoch Porn Again Church of Sun Worshippers in California.

WE'RE ALL GOING ON A FREE SUMMER HOLIDAY!

You all know that my favourite holiday resort is Cliff Richard's villa in Barbados. But I bet you didn't know that St Albion's most famous ex-chorister could soon be living in abject luxury, simply due to a silly law about the copyright of his wonderful records that have given people so much pleasure over the years. Can you believe it?

Please help by joining the vicar's petition to save poor Cliff. Just sign below and make sure this "Bachelor Boy" has a "Living Wage"!! T.B.

I think Sir Cliff should be given a peerage

Signed...

ST ALBION PARISH NEWS

18th August 2006

Acting Incumbent Dr J. Reid PhD (Gorbals)

IMPORTANT ANNOUNCEMENT BY MR PRESCOTT

I would like to make it incumbently clear that during the vicar's absence I am the person in charge NOT Mr Reid. Mr Reid is merely

We regret that due to pressures of space it has not been possible to print Mr Prescott's statement in full.

John Reid

The Vicar's message this week has been sent by email from Barbados

Hi to all of you back home! And I want to make one thing clear right from the start – that because I happen to be a long, long way away doesn't mean that I am not right there with you, sharing your fears, hoping your hopes and dreaming your dreams!

But, most importantly, I am still very much in charge, on a hands-on, day-to-day basis.

The last thing I want to do is to suggest that Mr Prescott isn't doing a first-rate job!

But the truth is that he really isn't doing the job at all!

I mean, I know a lot of you have been a bit concerned about leaving John in change – and I understand that!

After all, someone who sleeps around with his secretary and spends the afternoon playing croquet when he should be at work, is hardly the ideal person to be given such a heavy responsibility.

But that's exactly the point. John isn't in charge. I am, as I said earlier. And remember who it was who said "I am with you always"? It was me! And that's still my message.

So, not only am I recharging my batteries for all the vital parish work that lies ahead, as I sit here by the pool, I am also working 24/7, keeping in minute-by-minute touch with all sorts of important people all over the world, who look to me for guidance and help in these troubled times!

Take today, for instance. Here is a print-out of everything I have been doing for the parish since I got out of bed at 6.30 to do my

The Vicar hard at work, as seen by local artist Mr de la Nougerede

exercises (not, I hasten to add, that I need to do exercises, since I am 100 percent fighting fit, as you have to be to do my job, otherwise I might end up looking like poor Mr Clarke, before we sadly had to let him go from running the Neighbourhood Watch)!

6.31 am Put through call to Rev. Dubya for an update on oecumenical matters, such as our joint mission to Iraq, Lebanon, Iran, etc, etc. Message on answering machine as follows: *Greetings in the name of the Lord! You have reached the voicemail of the Rev. Dubya Bush. Kindly leave your message after the bleep.* I leave a message, asking him to ring me back as soon as possible.

6.40 am Breakfast on mango segments and shark fin toast.

8.15 am Put through call to my good friend Bishop Kofi Annan of the First Church of the United Nations in New York. Message: *Bishop Annan is taking no calls at this time, due to pressure of work.*

9.30 am Attempted to track down someone in Lebanon who could brief me on the situation. But unfortunately all lines to that country seem to be out of order.

10 am Tried to call Mr Prescott about something I saw about Heathrow on CNN in my bedroom in the villa. After a very long wait, it was answered by Mrs Potts, who I remembered does the cleaning on Tuesdays at the Working Men's Club. "Oh, hullo, vicar," she said. "I thought you was on holiday." I told her to put Mr Prescott on the phone. "I can't do that," she said. "He's gone down the park to play croquet with his new secretary."

11 am Called the vicarage on the off-chance that someone might be there. The phone was answered by Dr Reid, who told me not to worry and that everything was under control. He was adamant that I did not need to come back from holiday – not that it is a holiday since, as you can see, I am working flat out!

I think this is enough to show how very much I've still got my finger on the pulse when it comes to parish affairs, and I know how much this is appreciated by many of you back home!

With you always,

Tony

My Holiday
by Mrs Beckett

Everyone has their own idea of what makes a perfect holiday. Some like to fly off to faraway places and stay in the houses of their rich friends. Others prefer to stay at home to play croquet with their new secretaries! But for me and my husband Leo, the ideal holiday is a homely caravan and a welcoming camp site, somewhere in the French countryside, furnished with all the essentials, such as toilets, shower facilities and a little shop.

For a start, a caravan holiday cuts across class barriers, something our church used to be in favour of! And in these days, when we're all so much aware of the threat to the planet, there's a big difference between our humble caravan and a huge jumbo jet flying to the West Indies, pumping out millions of tons of poisonous gases which will melt the ice caps and drown millions of innocent fish. So take a leaf out of the Beckett book. All you need is a simple 40-foot six-berth mobile home and, of course, a car powerful enough to pull 300 tons, and it's hurrah for the open road!

● *PS. Another advantage of caravanning is that you can easily return from holiday if there is a crisis, rather than being stuck on a yacht, swanning about in silly flowered trunks!*

Text of the Week with Dr John Reid

This week I've chosen some comforting words from Scripture, which I think will make everyone feel much better:

"Don't panic, Mr Mainwaring" (Book of Jones, 7.3).

ST ALBION PARISH NEWS

1st September 2006

Hullo!

Or should I say, "yo, everybody", as we say in Barbados, where as you know I've spent a few days recharging my batteries!

And many thanks, by the way, to Mr Reid for standing in so capably for Mr Prescott during my absence!

Not that I was really absent, because as I told you last time, I managed to keep in 24/7 touch with parish affairs (even when I was scuba diving!).

But now I'm back in the vicarage, I can see that there is a great deal for me to do.

And no, that doesn't include "retiring", as our friend in Tesco rather rudely suggested, shortly before he fell into the demonstration "Barbecue Pit" which were on special End-of-Summer offer at "£5.99 – Buy One, Get Three Free".

No, whatever the mutterings around the parish, even among one or two members of the PCC, I am not "in the Departure Lounge"!

In fact, I haven't even been through "Security" yet – and that, as we all know, takes a very long time these days!

No, I want to make it clear that, as I return to the fray, I have never felt fitter, healthier or, dare I say it, sexier (and let me hasten to add that it wasn't me who said it, it was our host Sir Cliff, as we sat on the verandah one night after Cherie had gone to bed!).

I think this "holiday snap" that Mr Campbell kindly developed for me with his new "Photoshop" device says it all!

And what, I ask you, is the first job on my "to do" list for the days that lie ahead?

Number One must be to bring peace to the warring nations of the Holy Land.

We have all found it rather embarrassing to see our friend Monsignor Chirac trying to "step in" with his offers of unlimited help, when all it turned out to amount to was sending a couple of baguettes, a few smelly cheeses, a string of onions and a small box of waterproof plasters!

No disrespect to the Monsignor, but I can't see this making much contribution to the peace process! In fact, frankly, I thought our friend Jacques was left looking like a bit of an idiot, with a generous helping of scrambled oeuf on his silly face!

What is really required here is for a major figure on the world ecumenical stage to offer to go out in person and bring all the quarrelling parties round the table, just as I did on our successful mission to St Gerry's in Belfast.

That is why I have let it be known to everyone in the Holy Land, whether they be Jew, Christian or Muslim, that I am personally ready to fly out at any time to meet them all.

In the words of that great hymn written by the saints Peter, Paul and Mary, "All my bags are packed, I'm ready to go. The taxi's waiting, he's blowing his horn."

Inspiring lines, aren't they?

So I've done everything I can, and I'm not going to get upset if people say, "No thanks, vicar, we don't want you over here, you would only make things worse."

Look, if those guys in Lebanon don't want me to sort out their problems for them, that's their perfect right!

I'm the first to put up my hand and say, "Yes, I understand! I feel your pain! I know where you're coming from! I hear what you say!" (From the *Pleatitudes*, taken from the *Gospel According to St Matthew Parris*.)

So don't think for a minute that I am in any way offended when a bunch of small-minded, ungrateful Lebanese troublemakers ignore my generous offer to solve all their problems!

Of course I don't mind. I don't even mind when they accuse me of siding with Rabbi Ehud and the Rev. Dubya in an attempt to destroy them!

Stupid or what? Anyway, if they don't want me, I'd like them to know that I've still got plenty of very important things to do back here in the parish!

Top of the list is the need to streamline our parish outing, to avoid any repetition of that thoroughly unnecessary incident at Brighton last year when we had to eject a senile old gentleman, Mr Wolfgang, for making pro-terrorist comments while Mr Straw was trying to remember what the Rev. Dubya had told me to tell him to say!

Well, it's not going to happen again! My plan is as follows:

To ensure that only bona-fide loyal parishioners are allowed onto the charabanc, we will be introducing a new "security system" and people will not be allowed to bring onto the coach any bottles of alcohol (sorry Mr Marshall-Andrews, but we don't want you starting one of your usual fights on the way home!).

The following items of hand luggage will, however, be allowed, if carried in a see-through bag: (i) copies of Cherie's book *I Am A Goldfish: Life Inside the Vicarage*; (ii) I ♥ Dubya baseball caps; (iii) cheque books and credit cards. (Thanks to Mr Reid for putting this security package together!)

And by the way, we all want to have fun but, watch out everyone, not too many ice creams and chips, or you'll come home looking like Mr Prescott! And you wouldn't want to see a picture of him in his bathing suit in this newsletter, would you? Urgh! (No offence, John!)

So, I've appointed Mrs Flint to be the parish's first-ever "Obesity Czar", to go round handing out spot fines to anyone who has a body mass index of more than 27.34! Caroline is also going to be slapping a new kind of order on offenders, like an ASBO but renamed a "FATSO"!, which will keep overweight parishioners off the streets!

I look forward to seeing everyone on the outing and I hereby pledge that I will not speak for more than two hours! (Including an hour for applause).

See yo all there!

Yours,

Tony

FORTHCOMING EVENTS

A real highlight of this autumn will be readings from the private diaries of Mr Blunkett, formerly head of our Neighbourhood Watch.

Mr Blunkett will be reading extracts in the Village Hall on Tuesday, Wednesday and Thursday evenings, 7pm-10pm, between 24 September and 24 December. He promises to "really spill the beans" on what really went on behind the scenes during his tempestuous relationship with Mrs Kimberly Quinn!

Adults only. Half price to any single ladies of the parish who would like to have his babies! T.B.

NEWS FROM THE TREASURER

I expect many of you have recently received this lovely card sent out by our treasurer Mr Brown, showing off his new family! But where have we seen this idea before? Oh yes, doesn't it rather remind us of the cards Cherie and I used to send out at Christmas-time in the years after Leo was born? I'm not of course suggesting that Mr Brown has copied my idea in some kind of mistaken bid for popularity. But isn't that the first thought that might come into anyone's mind?

And really, Gordon, it's asking a bit much of people to believe that you really look as young as you do in this picture. You really mustn't be surprised if people say that you've doctored the picture with this new Photoshop device. Who do you think you are, Gordon? Posh Spice? You should spend rather more time trying to sort out those accounts and rather less time worrying about how old you look! T.B.

PS: No offence, Gordon!

SPECIAL OFFER!

Many of you were kind enough to say how much you liked the vicar's "Anthony" mug which he has been drinking from recently. Now the newsletter is offering a special "Gordon" mug (or "Smug" as I call it!!)

Here is the design by local artist Mr Newman. Anyone who wants one should write at once to their psychiatrist! T.B.

ST ALBION PARISH NEWS

15th September 2006

Hullo!

And I'd like to begin with an apology to the parish. I'm really sorry that other people have behaved so badly. Honestly, what must they think of us, when they see their popular, charismatic and successful vicar being attacked for no reason at all?

Yes, I'm sorry for this shameful behaviour and I don't mind being the one to take the blame and apologise on their behalf.

In the ten long years I have spent serving this parish 9/11 *(Surely 24/7? Ed.)*, never in my wildest imaginings could I have imagined that some members of my own flock, who owe everything to my stewardship of St Albion's, would turn on me and try to force me out of my own vicarage!

These were the very people I had nurtured like a good shepherd caring for his sheep.

And if one went astray, as they often did, I did not leave them to become the prey of hungry wolves. I sought them out and brought them back into the fold – some of them many times, as Mr Blunkett, Mr Mandelson, Mr Byers and Mr Prescott would be the first to testify!

I am not going to name names – as you know, that has never been my policy – and, in any case, the individual I am going to name is someone who plays such an insignificant part in parish life that you will not have heard of him.

And neither had I, until last week when, out of the blue, he wrote me a very rude and unhelpful letter, to say that unless I resigned as vicar, he would feel obliged to stand down from his duties photocopying this newsletter and stapling it together before Mrs Blears delivers it on her bike.

The name of this poisonous little nobody is Tom Watson.

Tom who? I hear you ask. Exactly! Which is why I was planning to sack him in any case, even though I hadn't heard of him!

Now, of course, his name will be remembered for ever more, whenever the subject of treachery is raised.

I gather also that there has been tittle-tattle in the Britannia Arms, saying that the Treasurer, Mr Brown, was actually behind Mr Watson's letter and that Gordon was hatching some sort of plot against me.

But Gordon has given me his word that he had nothing to do

with it and I fully accept his assurance, even though I don't believe a word of it.

Mr Brown's story, that Mr Watson drove 200 miles to drop in on Gordon's holiday home in the Isle of Dull just to take a cuddly toy for little Angus, is, of course, ridiculous.

But I am happy to accept that this is indeed what happened – even though it didn't. Likewise, Gordon's claim that he was smiling about his new baby when he left the vicarage, having told me to pack my bags and give him the key, is patently untrue. Though, once again, I am happy to accept that this is indeed what happened – even though it clearly didn't.

But enough of this. I know that you are all heartily sick of this silly squabbling. You want more than anything to draw a line under this and to move on. I know you do. So let's draw up a timetable but a **real** timetable of what the parish needs to achieve.

1. Peace in the Holy Land. Doesn't even the mention of my mission to the Middle East make some of you feel ashamed for your small-mindedness? Hey, let's open that window of opportunity and let the dove of peace fly in – or out, as the case may be.

2. And what about our new Primark Beacon Technology Academy? And our new Burger King Hospital, motto: *Fat For Purpose*? And what about the criminal gangs roaming around the recreation ground frightening old ladies?

3. And what about all the other things that need to be done, like turning the Millennium Tent into a Super Casino, bringing much-needed gambling to the parish?

That's what I know you are really concerned about – not a lot of silly gossip about personalities. As I said, we've moved on from that and drawn a line under it. Particularly, Gordon and his friends.

Shall I tell you a story from the Bible? There was once a just and holy man who went about doing good. Some said he was the Messiah, though he was too modest to accept this description. And he went about performing miracles. But then one of his disciples betrayed his leader after they broke bread together in the upper room of a fashionable restaurant. And then do you know what happened? He took his own life, so disgusted was he by his own treachery.

It's not a nice story, is it, but it may serve as a warning to others who are considering betraying their spiritual leader. So let's hear no more of the tawdry tittle-tattle and concentrate on the important job of making sure that Gordon Brown never becomes Vicar.

Yours,

Tony

Parish Postbag

Dear Vicar,
    After long and careful thought, we the undersigned feel that it is time for the vicar to
        Yours sincerely,
        Jim Nobody, Sid Loser,
        Mike Hasbeen and Sue Saddo

■ **This letter has been cut for reasons of space and some of the names of the writers have been changed to protect their identities and to make them look silly. T.B.**

Dear Vicar,
    I would like to put on record how much I hate Gordon Brown. He is stupid, stupid, stupid. And I have nothing but total contempt for this looney loser, who is unfit to even think about being vicar.
        Yours sincerely,
        Charles Clarke,
        c/o Oddbins, Tesco Road

■ **For reasons of space, this letter has been printed in full. T.B.**

Dear Sir,
    Whilst not wishing to add to the unhelpful controversy over the parish leadership, may I just offer my conviction that Mr Brown is not only "autistic", but a manic depressive, a sufferer from Tourette's and a dangerous psychopathic who should never have been released into the community.
    It gives me no pleasure to write this, but ha ha ha ha ha ha ha ha.
        Yours,
        P. Mandelson,
        Rue des Matelots, Bruxelles.

New Faces On The PCC

Many of you will have noticed in the last week that wherever I go, I am accompanied by a charming, well-groomed, smartly-dressed and English man. His name is Alan Johnson and you'll be seeing a lot more of Alan (solid English name, note!) in the future.

He's got a lot to offer. First of all, he's English. Secondly, he's not Scottish. And, thirdly, he's not called Gordon.

Welcome aboard, Alan. Good to have you in the team. And you have many of the qualities that make a good vicar. You're English, not Scottish and *(You've said this. Ed.)*

A FINAL THOUGHT...

How Things Would Be Different Under Gordon

My policy, like any good vicar, is always to drink tea. But Gordon, as you can clearly see, prefers black coffee. This explains why he is always so nervous, twitchy, sweaty, untrustworthy and unsuitable to be the vicar! After all no-one is ever going to say 'More tea, vicar?' to a man like Gordon, are they?
        Tony Blair